Through the Hangar Doors

Through the Hangar Doors

by

Fred Adkin

To Service ground crew everywhere

Airlife

England

by the same author:
FROM THE GROUND UP

Copyright © 1986 F. J. Adkin

ISBN 0 906393 59 0

First published 1986
by Airlife Publishing Ltd.

Printed in England by Livesey Ltd., Shrewsbury.

Airlife Publishing Ltd.

7 St. John's Hill, Shrewsbury, England.

Contents

Bibliography

Pictorial History of the RAF. Phillip Moyes; W. R. Taylor. Ian Allan 1968.

The Royal Air Force – the first 30 years. A. G. Trevenan James. McDonald and James 1976.

The Royal Air Force – the first 50 years. Charles Sims. Adam and Charles Black 1968.

The Malayan Emergency 1948-1960. Ministry of Defence 1970.

Flight from the Middle East. Air Chief Marshal Sir David Lee CBE, CB. Ministry of Defence 1978.

Jet. Sir Frank Whittle. Muller 1951.

Aircraft of the Royal Air Force. Owen Thetford. Putnam 1968.

The Role of the Bomber. W. Ronald Clark. Sedgwick and Jackson 1977.

Not much of an Engineer. Sir Stanley Hooker. Airlife 1984.

Service to the Services. Harry Miller. Newman Neame 1971.

The Benson Report 1954. Ministry of Defence.

Berlin Airlift. HMSO 1949.

Royal Air Force Yearbooks.

Royal Air Forces Quarterly.

Royal Air Force News.

Acknowledgements

Most authors of non-fiction books require the help of those staff of research organisations with specialist knowledge and this author is no different. I express my sincere thanks to all those who gave their help so freely, including the other rank contributors without whom the book would have no human touch and who are 'starred' in the index; they will know my gratitude for their help. Although all were helpful, a few of the organisations must be mentioned:

The Air Historical Branch, whose friendly team assists all who seek their help.

C. C. H. Cole, aviation historian, who broached the setting up of the Benson Experiment; Air Commodore F. J. Manning, CB, CBE, Chairman of the Benson Experiment, who made important documentation available which formed the basis of Chapter 6 and Miss Jane Redford of Common Services (PS) Copyright Section MoD, for permission to reproduce extracts from that documentation.

The Station Commander of RAF Finningley and S/Ldr D. A. Exley, MBE, who opened the doors on that station to make Chapter 8 possible, with special thanks to the Station Photographic Section who supplied the photos to illustrate it.

Bruce Robertson, aviation historian, who helped keep the book on track with a preliminary edit and who supplied photographs. A. Williams of the Imperial War Museum Department of Photographs. R. W. Mack of the Royal Air Force Museum Photographic Section. Bill Ayliffe who carried out a final editing and made some useful suggestions.

J. T. Dawkins and Doris Courtnage of the Inspector of Recruiting Photo Library.

To the following who helped unstintingly:- F/Lt J. P. Goss, RAF St. Athan; F/O K. W. Davies, RAF Hereford; F/Lt D. Brown, WRAF, Directorate of Public Relations; F/Lt R. Shepherd, P7A MoD; Sgt Bill Kershaw, RAF Mount Batten; Cpl Simon Ellis ABIPP, RAF Official; Mr. L. F. Moulton, Union Jack Club; Mr. N. Trowell, NAAFI Collection. My wife, who helped as assiduously with this book as with the first.

Foreword

This book continues the history of RAF ground tradesmen from the period described in *From the Ground Up (1862-1945)*, from 1945 to the present day. At the end of the Second World War the Royal Air Force was at the pinnacle of its operational efficiency, one of the three great air forces of the world which had contributed materially to the overall victory. The German Air Force was no less great but was on the losing side. Within a year of VJ Day the RAF was but a shadow of its wartime self.

The post-war period was concerned with the efforts of the airmen and airwomen under Air Ministry and Air Force Department planning to rebuild the RAF, not to its former size, which it will never reach again, but to an efficiency that surpasses even that of the great days — and achieving it against a background of crises, crippling economic impositions and restricted manpower. And it is this manpower — this broad base — that has contributed so much to the present rebuild, the changes in the trade structure, the WRAF's complete involvement when they were integrated into the RAF, constant postings overseas to areas of strife, the manning of RAF Germany to NATO requirements and many other events.

This account tells of their contribution in all the major — and some of the minor — events that befell the RAF, but with almost 40 years of history to be compressed into 170 pages the detail cannot be as deep as desired. A wish to change the standard of conditions of service for the airmen and airwomen to meet modern requirements has long been the aim of far-sighted authority and in 1954 the first definite, successful steps were taken to make the RAF a service for a career man to consider seriously.

The term 'other ranks' is now officially frowned on and they are now known collectively as airmen and airwomen. Likewise, the modern airmen does not seem all that keen on being referred to as an erk, feeling perhaps that, while it denotes other ranks of an older generation, it does not suit the image of today's high-tech sophisticated tradesman with his greater freedom. That may be, but who knows — today's skilled tradesmen were once yesterday's erks who helped put the RAF squarely in the forefront of military air forces. There's no reason to suppose that today's technicians won't keep it there.

Chapter 1
Rebuild from Greatness

Near the war's end participating nations were reeling from the exhaustion of manpower losses and facing financial near-disaster, with many cities in ruins, massive losses of military equipment, all still to be paid for, and economic losses of staggering magnitude.

The world's greatest independent air force, along with the greatest military air force, had bombed Germany into submission, aided by the superb ground and naval forces of all the Allies. It had taken six years and in that time Germany had withstood the combined might of several major Western nations, the overwhelming resources of the USA and the ferocity of Russia. The West had begun to concentrate all of its forces against an equally tough but even more ferocious Japan when World War Two was abruptly ended by the most self-destructive weapon man had devised and used on himself — the atom bomb.

Just before the end of war in Europe, Allied forces had overrun the German prison camps and a high priority was given to get these men home. The ending of the war against Japan gave rise to a similar situation in the East, but the POWs there were in a far more debilitated condition; so much so that it was essential to get these unfortunate men and women home quickly to the caring comfort of their own country. Which presented a problem. Britain was short of transport aircraft and all available troop ships were being used to bring home the service men and women for demobilisation. The dilemma was in deciding priorities. The Government decided that the POWs from the Japanese theatre were the more important and immediately every effort was bent towards this operation. Suitable aircraft that could carry a sizeable number of people with their kit, however uncomfortably, had their interiors stripped

out as far as possible and a form of primitive seating installed.

Unfortunately, there were insufficient numbers of such aircraft and it was decided to delay the demob of tradesmen of the few squadrons that had suitable aircraft and whose disbandment would affect the operation. The consequent delay in demob caused considerable discontent which, coupled with bad conditions and overcrowding, and believed to have been flashed off by a Communist cell run by an LAC, had reached a point where token demonstrations were made by some airmen in Iraq, India and Singapore. At these places the Riot Act was read out by senior officers — with mixed results — and the so-called 'mutiny' was ended by the Government's tough stand and by the refusal of most airmen on the Iraq stations to participate. The Government had decided that the unrest would be considered as mutinous if it continued. It is quite possible that had the airmen been informed of the reason for the delay in demob plans the discontent might have been about conditions only. The unrest subsided and at the end the (unknown) ringleaders do not seem to have been charged.

The effort to bring home POWs became a major operation under the command of Air Vice-Marshal Bennett, and thousands were flown home, mainly in Dakotas, Yorks and Lancasters from Europe and in Liberators (aptly named) from the Far East. Despite impressing as much sea transport as possible it took nearly a year before the POW operation was completed.

During this humanitarian operation Britain's forces were being demobilised from a major war for the third time in half a century. This time the lessons of 1918 had been well learned and in general the country

Allied POWs from Bangkok being flown out to Rangoon in No. 7 Command aircraft for onward passage to their countries. 60 aircraft flew out 1000 per day on this route. 1945. (IWM.)

was ready for the return of the service men and women and had employment for them. To ensure fair operation of demob a 'first in first out' scheme had been instituted and depots were sited, ready stocked with civilian clothes, at regional points.

Newly arrived demobees went immediately through the planned procedure, giving particulars on arrival and handing in all equipment, receiving a railway warrant and an initial cash payment, and a meal if required. Then straight to the large sheds where stocks of clothes awaited. Some variety was evident and an airman could select a passable sports coat and flannels and an even more passable suit (some said that's what the clothes were — passable!). Everything a man would need was supplied, including a serviceable raincoat. Laden with these items,

the airman staggered to the exit end of the store where the clothes were quickly packed into a stout cardboard box. From the store, as soon as sufficient numbers were ready, they boarded service transport which took them to the nearest station. From here they were on their own — free?

The scheme worked well, except for the delay in bringing home service men and women from the more far-flung outposts of what had been the Empire where admin matters were more difficult, or from major battle theatres where transports were strained to the limit to return the vast numbers quickly; Burma and the Middle East were extreme examples. To give the men and women a little assistance in settling down, all ranks were awarded a hard-won Bounty, based on service and rank. Not a lot, but it did help some. Numbers of enterprising types revealed entrepreneurial talent engendered by their service experiences and turned the bounty into successful enterprises.

The rapid removal of nearly a million men and women from its strength by demobilisation placed a heavy strain on the RAF as it faced the task of rebuilding a peace-time air force. With large numbers of the various trades leaving in such a short time the result was to create an imbalance of trades, which upset the plans of the Air Staff who had tried to ensure that capability for any probable operation could be retained.

The Air Staff had prepared a preliminary recruiting scheme in the closing months of the war. Selected tradesmen were given the choice of signing-on to complete 24 years, providing they were on a regular pre-war engagement and were at least Corporals, had completed seven years' service and would not be over the age of 55 at the end of 24 years. During this period the RAF accepted volunteer tradesmen direct to the equivalent Trade Groups A and B without technical training, provided that they passed a comprehensive trade test, as a temporary means of getting skilled men into units to replace those demobbed. Immediate post-war recruiting was limited to four periods of engagement; three were for a total of 12 years, comprising 8, 9 or 10 years' regular service followed by the remaining years, to complete 12, on the reserve; e.g. 8 years' regular, 4 years' reserve. The fourth engagement was for one of 12 years from the age of 18 for apprentices, who joined at the age of 15½ or 16.

*   *   *   *   *

Complete with kit bags, Allied prisoners of war are seen walking past a line of RAF Stirlings to the aircraft which were to fly them back to the United Kingdom.

This transitional period was one for the making of a major decision by some and our mythical Joe Soap illustrates a problem familiar to many. Corporal Joe Soap stood at a personal crossroads and after 5½ years of war service, a couple of campaigns and promotion well earned, had to decide — civvy street or stay in the mob. The decision required deep consideration.

His war service had been necessary and enthusiastically entered into, its commitment the average of most who served; he had endured long hours, boredom and occasional action at home and overseas. He had seen parts of the world unknown even to his school geography master and had made many good, but transient, friends. He had sweated and gone hungry, seen friends killed and injured in the desert and been many times short of cash. Technically, as a Group A tradesman, he had been well trained, in constant contact with his trade and kept up to date in it by service literature and the odd manufacturer's course; in peace-time service he could expect more 'bull', stronger discipline, a far longer and harder task to gain promotion. He could also expect at least one more overseas tour and the inevitable unit postings, more service friendships and, if he wanted it so much, security.

Poor old Joe. He was the epitome of many hundreds of airmen and airwomen who were soon to be faced with similar decisions.

*   *   *   *   *

To keep the service going during this transition period between demob and rebuild, heavy reliance was placed on signed-on 'hostilities only' airmen, a thin layer of new direct entry recruits, a solid back-up of experienced senior NCOs and National Service airmen (NSA).

National Service was introduced in 1947 as a recruitment stopgap and those called up in 1947 served for two years, with training in a trade decided by the recruiting authority.

Quite a large number of NSA were sent overseas. Their short period of service meant that there would be little or no promotion. Those few who decided that they liked the life took up the option offered them of signing on to complete six years, which gave them the opportunity of advanced trade training and subsequent promotion.

The NSA Scheme was not a great success for there was much moaning by some of these airmen, who cursed the service and did as little work as possible. These attitudes were possibly brought on by seeing returning troops entering civilian employment and, as they thought, taking their jobs (they had a point); conscription itself; the return to peace offering no stimulus to make their impressment worthwhile; and the attitudes of some serving airmen and NCOs towards them. The apathetic and sometimes 'bolshie' outlook of these airmen increased the work load of many of their own who genuinely enjoyed their service and added unnecessary mental strain to those NCOs who often leaned over backwards to make the recalcitrant realise how much they were needed by the RAF and the country. But the conscript's new attitude of not taking orders at face value and habit of asking 'Why?' rubbed off onto the new regular generation of erks and made them more independently minded.

Having said that, it must be stressed that the greater majority were genuine, hard-working young men who accepted their responsibilities and the situation they had been put into. The author had considerable experience with NSA both on home and overseas units and found that, in general, they were no different from other, regular, airmen. It was the conditions created by the restrictions of their conscription that was really the problem. With only one-and-a-half or two years to serve, they had had only a short trade course, had often been posted overseas immediately and had to face the odd snide remark from the ignorant. But the RAF had its recruiting money's worth at the time when they were needed and it was in this context, the early days, that they so proved their worth.

The year of 1948 was one of great crises for this was the year when a 'hot' campaign began in Malaya, and the Berlin Airlift, the first of the 'cold war' confrontations, followed within a month. These two crises immediately raised a problem of manpower shortage which was compounded by unsatisfactory recruiting levels. Both events needed large numbers of trained and experienced tradesmen, but these were just not readily available. The squadrons involved in the Malayan Emergency naturally wanted to hold onto, and increase, their manpower against the demands of the Airlift. In addition, large transport aircraft were needed on the Airlift but were also needed to carry supplies to Malaya. The Air Staff gave priority to Berlin, diverted all large transport aircraft to German and combed all units for suitable tradesmen for posting onto the Airlift. Both crises absorbed many tradesmen and as a result a shortage soon developed of trained airmen.

As a consequence a Trade Structure Committee was set up in the same year to prepare a new recruiting drive for the years ahead. The aims of the committee were:

1. To conserve skill and increase efficiency by directing men and women to work where they were best suited.
2. To direct men and women to differing fields of activity within their trades to widen their experience.

The reasons given for these aims were:

a) the continuing cold war.
b) unsettled world conditions.
c) the growing complexity of aircraft equipment and operational aids.
d) full civilian employment.
e) the need for a larger force.
f) retiring on a full pension at age 40 was no longer economical to the RAF.

And, of course, there was the requirement to provide technical manpower for the two crises.

After the war, being married in the RAF became a major problem both to the airman (or airwoman) and to the RAF. There was a

All, except N. I. Smith and author on right, are National Service (the majority) or short service airmen of No. 13 Squadron at RAF Fayid in 1949, who did a remarkably fine job. (Author.)

hope by most married personnel that they could soon be together, but this was not to be. Being granted married quarters was an extremely slow procedure, some not getting one until well in the 1950s, others not at all. Quite a few left the service for this reason alone.

The main reason for this not unexpected state of affairs was the insufficient number of married quarters available, a legacy from a pre-war air force which had only had an average strength of about 35,000 based on small stations with consequently few quarters. Now, having to house the married airmen from a force ten times the size, plus the lowering of the official marriage age — which had been 26 before the war — it was just impossible to find homes for them.

Many young couples tried to live out locally on their grossly inadequate pay and many were 'ripped off' by their grasping landlords, who very quickly forgot the tremendous part played by the services on their behalf. The RAF instituted a crash programme for building MQs and an increase in marriage allowance to ease the cost of living out. But it was not until the opposing forces of more MQs and diminishing manpower balanced

This photograph shows well the ground support equipment required for a quick turnround on the staging post at RAF Fayid in 1949, including the number of ground crew. Note the World War 2 vintage fire extinguisher. (Noble).

each other that the position eased. The new MQs were aimed directly at influencing young married airmen to stay on in the RAF. It succeeded to a large extent, once the difficult years were passed. Now, almost every station has no problem from this source and the families are well catered for in almost every respect.

In fact, as the building programme was completed and as manpower decreased (the continual RAF bogey), so many MQs became available that eventually the reverse conditions applied and a number of MQs were standing empty on little-used stations. This particular problem was partially solved when some of the stations were returned to local councils; for example, RAF Worthy Down became a large housing estate, RAF Hooton Park was used for the erection of fuel oil tanks, RAF Honiley returned to the land with its quarters used by civilians and RAF Oakington was handed over to the army. A

number of RAF stations such as Aldergrove, Hawarden and Castle Bromwich became civil airports.

Recruiting was disappointing in 1948 — it had fallen to around 700, including WAAF, per week — and drastic measures were required to slow the overall decline in annual numbers from the recruiting centres of about 150,000 out of which 35,000 to 40,000 were NSA in low-grade trades. The main causes for the decline were full employment in civilian industry and the real possibility of new recruits being quickly posted overseas.

By 1948 Britain was also involved with the Western Union, precursor of NATO, and was required to have squadrons stationed in Europe as part of the multinational defence against possible dangers from the East. The manpower shortage was made worse by the attitude of a government which seemingly ignored the dangerous levels in the face of Britain's commitments overseas, using a

This scene of No. 8 Squadron Vampire FB9 activity at RAF Amman in 1952 was typical of the period. The aircraft are being serviced, the equipment making an untidy clutter on the tarmac. Behind the refueller is a Mk. 19 Anson, the 'workhorse' of that period. (J. Cowburn).

modified version of the pre-war Ten Year Rule to batter the armed services with: 'There is no war expected for the next 10 years and we haven't got the money'. For the next 10 years at least, the experience of Joe Soap and his kind was going to be vital to the rebuild of the RAF, for those years were to be chaotic. But the chaos was skilfully controlled by the Air Staff: they calculated, schemed, planned, plugged here, withdrew there and manoeuvred the RAF through a difficult period, a peace-time planner's nightmare, to overcome the effect of so much lethargy.

The WAAF had some satisfaction in that after the war they were not disbanded, as were their predecessors in 1920, but were recognised for the tremendous effort they had achieved, particularly in the UK when they had successfully shouldered so much of the load and proved that they were equal to the men in many jobs. Despite a slight whiff of male chauvinism in the Air Ministry they were incorporated into the RAF as an integral part of that service in February 1949 as the Women's Royal Air Force (WRAF).

The organisation of the WRAF took a slightly different turn after its integration, mainly in its trade structure, because the demand of the new jet aircraft required a standard in some of the trades that the WRAF, with respect, were quite untrained for. However, the women were employed in the highly skilled trades for which they were more suitable. In addition they supplied the right kind of temperament to take a high place in the administration and organisation of the

RAF in such fields as pay accounts, clerical work, telecommunications, radar, catering, MT, ATC, photography, ground signalling, medical and dental, safety equipment and so on.

A factor often overlooked in any history of ground crew tradesmen is the vital and increasing part played by WRAF in radar, the control by radio of aircraft and the global communications network that has steadily developed since WW2. The whole world knows, and rightly so, of the wartime WAAF plotters at work on the map table, with Sir up in the gallery monitoring an aerial engagement scores of miles away. How many know of their work behind the scenes on operational stations, telexing, telephoning, sending thousands of signals, servicing the equipment, keeping the data boards up to date, testing and operating the radio links and passing messages from the Ministry of Defence to all points? The WRAF have now become essential to the efficient running of this side of the RAF.

A WRAF SAC telecommunications operator at work on a teleprinter unit. 1977. (MOD.)

The photograph shows a PR34A of No. 13 Squadron based on RAF Fayid undergoing a 'bull' session to maintain the RAF's creed of immaculate aircraft. The PR34A in the hangar is on routine daily servicing. The photograph also shows the camera bay bulge, behind the entrance ladder, with the camera windows. (Author).

Today, the WRAF are truly integrated into the service. WRAF Senior NCOs are in charge of Sections and — a most memorable event — the first WRAF Station Warrant Officer, WO Jenny Winspear, was appointed to RAF Benson in 1984. Ironically this station was the site of the Benson Experiment which helped to break some of the older, and unwanted, traditions. Many an old sweat must have made a pithy comment in the Mess on this one. But the fact that the RAF assessed her as suitable is an indication that women are no longer considered as second-class citizens. It is also an indication of what is possible to any woman with determination and the right qualifications.

In 1949 the NSA intake was raised to an estimated 45,000 from whom were drawn the new Assistant trades, destined for the armament, airframe, electrical, instrument, air and ground wireless and radar trades. An official working party was set up to report the effects of training the NSA to service and operate one type of equipment only. Their findings included the following:

more short courses were recommended;
the equipment the NSA would be trained on could soon go out of service;
NSA had to be posted only to those units that operated the equipment;
NSA sometimes returned to civilian life inadequately trained;
as equipment increased in specification it required more supervision; and, finally, the scheme was a waste of manpower.

Also in 1949 a Chief of Staff's Conference called 'Ariel' was held, in which manpower requirements were discussed. The conference was concerned with the lack of adequate reserves and the fact that more regular airmen were under training than had been allowed for, caused by the need to replace the 'war duration' men. Also, regular establishments were still undermanned, which meant that a larger proportion of NSA had to be accepted and the extra numbers created problems in Training Command. The whole range of 'other rank' problems was discussed, including manning, selection and allocation, careers, employment, trade training and reserves.

The first major step in the reorganisation of the trade structure to meet the anticipated future needs of a modern air force was the introduction of the 1951 Command/Technician Scheme which was quite revolutionary. Much new thought had been given to regulate and remove the anomalies that had infiltrated into a trade structure which had been laid down before the war. The new scheme was designed to produce tradesmen better adapted and trained to the future jet-orientated air force and its increasingly complex equipment.

The first great change was in the trade groups. The four overloaded groups that had existed so long were abolished and 22 compact groups were formed, within each of which were all the associated trades of that group and with each trade divided into Advanced and Skilled standards as applicable. The types of trades were also revised and updated. The new groups were:

1   Aircraft Engineering
2   Radio Engineering
3   Armament Engineering
4   Electrical and Instrument Engineering
5   General Engineering
6   Motor Transport Engineering
7   Marine Craft Engineering
8   Airfield Construction
9   Air Traffic Control and Fire Fighting
10 General Servicing
11 Ground Signalling
12 Security
13 Safety and Surface
14 Photography
15 Medical
16 Dental
17 Accounting and Secretarial
18 Supply
19 Catering
20 Police
21 Music
22 RAF Regiment

Groups 1 - 9 were similar to the old Group A and all tradesmen of that group were transferred to these, mostly in the Advanced category. In Groups 10 - 21 Advanced trades were introduced to give airmen and airwomen the opportunity of access to higher pay scales. The standards were roughly equivalent to their civilian counterparts. The new trade of Trade Assistant was to be trained 'on the job' at units until they had qualified for transfer to a skilled trade, in much the same way as the old ACH(GD) trade had done. Administrative Orderlies were classed as Trade Assistants.

The scheme also revolutionised the rank structure with a dual system based on administrative and technical qualities. All tradesmen were given the option of choosing their own 'ladder' into a Command or Technician group. Command NCOs would wear their stripes the normal way up and their main task within their trade was to act in an administrative and command capacity; to be in charge of a Flight or Section. Technicians would wear their stripes upside down; initially they were required to work in their particular trade and were issued with overalls and tool kits. This latter requirement did not go down well with many senior NCOs who were accustomed to the status of their previous rank and who had probably been in charge; they did not take kindly to putting on a pair of overalls and working alongside the lower ranks. At first, technicians were excused standard SNCO duties, which also caused some comment. Command SNCOs could order a Chief Technician to carry out work and detail a party of tradesmen for him. In the event of a desputed technical decision, this could be sought at a higher level (usually a Technical Officer).

Promotion in the case of the Command Career was by recommendation and merit, and for Technicians a minimum of five years was required between ranks, providing exams were passed in their trade. In the latter case it was necessary for Technicians to keep up-to-date in their trades in order to pass promotion exams. It was, of course, to the advantage of the Command NCOs to take whatever applicable courses were available in their basic trade and any specialist ones for their job as Command types. Subsequent revision altered the status and time limit for promotion of the Technician.

The scheme, however, was not seen as a success by the SNCOs. From the overlarge block of SNCOs approximately half remustered to Technicians and had initially to face five years before their next promotion, dependent on successful exam results. Many of the Command types, while apparently having a clearer path for promotion, were denied this by the shrinkage throughout the RAF of the number of units in the service. Against a fixed time limit for Technicians a Command Sgt Airframe Fitter, for example, might now have to wait until a Flt Sgt had either been promoted to WO (rare), completed his service, retired at the age of 55, or died, before he could hope for promotion; and anyway there were several Sgts to each Flt Sgt.

The early status requirements soon flopped and Senior and Chief Technicians were again acting in the same capacity as the Sergeants or

The DH Hornet, whose Merlins 130/131 are shown being serviced at RAF Fayid in 1949, is one of two Hornet-equipped Squadrons which flew out to Malaya for the Emergency. Although too late to see World War 2 service – the first Squadron was equipped in March 1946 – they proved excellent aircraft in the jungle with their rockets. The aircraft was also the last piston-engined fighter to enter RAF service. (Noble).

Flight Sergeants they were supposed to replace, which had the effect of weakening the authority, and promotion prospects, of Command NCOs. Consequently, the junior ranks gained very little promotion of their own in the first five years until the system was able to benefit as the SNCO block thinned out.

The official definition of the scheme was put briefly in an Air Ministry Order:

Career Command: those who, in addition to trade knowledge, are leaders and organisers for control and supervision.

Technicians: no room as SNCOs, great skill and specialist education quality.

Aircraftmen: competent but no ambition or capacity.

This latter description does seem unfair!

After an initial threefold increase in response to this scheme intake figures fluctuated to a high of around 1000 per week, then fell to 700 at the end of 1951, a drop which was presumed to be due to the low birthrate in 1933 and which was taken into consideration by Command and the Air Ministry.

For those WOs and SNCOs whose ambition extended beyond the Sergeants' Mess into the Officers' Mess an opportunity came in 1952, with the introduction of 'Branch' commissions, open to WOs, Flt Sgts and Chief Technicians. The commissions were in ground trades, were permanent, and required men with specialist trade qualifications plus the essential qualities of leadership and the ability to conduct themselves in the 'vaulted heavens' of the Officers' Mess.

The results were encouraging; Branch Officers became so essential to the RAF's progress in those difficult years that at its peak in 1970 commissions from the ranks comprised nearly one-third of the Engineering Branch. The scheme was a properly organised one; before, to gain a commission was rather more difficult and

often haphazard. A good percentage of pre-war ex-apprentices and quite a few direct entry tradesmen had already gained entry into the Officers' Mess by being in the right place at the right time. But, and this must be emphasised, they had all the necessary qualifications which, before the Branch scheme, were much higher. Promotion in the Branch scheme was very restricted, most officers rising only to Flight Lieutenant rank.

At about this time at RAF Lyneham, the Transport Command base, a Group Captain Manning inaugurated a scheme whereby the establishment was reduced to 75%, comprising a carefully balanced group of air and ground crew, and managed to increase flying activities by 150%. This success prompted the Air Member for Personnel, Sir Francis Fogarty, to form a special committee, aided by Science teams, to investigate conditions of service for other ranks with a view to increasing internal recruitment. The experiment began at RAF Benson in 1954 and is examined in detail in Chapter 6.

The beginning of the 1950s was also the beginning of many crises for the RAF — Aden, Korea, Kenya, Cyprus — and the Malaya Emergency was still going on and would do so until 1960. Suez in 1956 was to come. But the same period also saw the RAF emerging from its post-war dependence on old aircraft as the new jets, long projected, finally began to enter service and place the RAF once more in the front rank.

The year 1955 showed that the 1951 Trade Structure was not yet functioning as hoped. There was a shortage of skilled and, particularly, advanced tradesmen, which in the next few years was to be cured by the effects of the Benson Experiment. In the meantime the acute shortage of advanced tradesmen was compounded by their being used on supervisory duties and not applying their skills to the practical work in workshops, maintenance hangars and Sections. Much overtime was needed as a result. A few statistics give some idea of the manpower problem at that time, which was made worse by National Service and overseas commitments:

75% of other ranks were on engagements of 5 years or less;

50% were on National Service or three-year engagements.

In a six-month check, November 1953 to April 1954, it was found that:

13.4% of trained regulars were on the move, station to station;

10.7% of personnel were posted overseas (this was the period of the crises);

19.8% were on demobilisation.

The first of the debris to be swept away by the new Benson Broom was given public notice in the Air Estimates of 1957. As a result of this effort to make RAF tradesmen comparable with their equivalent in industry, not only in pay but also in conditions, a number of formerly accepted traditions were dropped.

During the next few years two factors emerged which had the effect of bringing about a better balance of manpower between trades. The first in 1957 was an edict affecting all other ranks of all the services: minimum pension time was reduced to 22 years and anyone wishing to do so could retire on completing this time. The RAF's manpower structure immediately benefited as numbers of long service SNCOs decided that there was little chance of further promotion and opted for retirement. The large blockage to promotion for the junior ranks was drastically reduced and they began to see their possibilities. The second occurred in 1961 when National Service was abolished and the RAF became an all-professional force, much to its advantage. From this date it had the great asset of voluntary enthusiasm from its new recruits and it could select the best and train them for the higher skills and longer periods of service. But, no surprise, at the end of 1960, just before the end of NS, checks revealed that the NSA had a slight edge over regulars in intelligence level but it was considered insufficient to affect the content of the training courses then in being. With the opportunity of selecting its own recruits more

carefully, the intelligence level of new airmen was soon seen to be higher than ever before.

Running in parallel with the Benson Experiment the Air Council enlisted top industrial brains from large concerns, in this case a Mr F. (later Sir Frederick) Hooper of Schweppes, to institute a course on management and human relations based on efficiency with economy, which eventually became the Man Management Course and was so successful that the other two services adapted it to their own special needs. The course is still in being and is an essential qualification for those SNCOs being considered for high promotion.

By the mid-fifties the sophisticated electronic equipment both on and off the aircraft, the large new engines and the new aircraft systems, such as powered controls, were all creating a need for specialists. The tradesmen of the older style were quite suitable for the propeller aircraft and the early jets, but the development of aircraft had increased dramatically. It was this requirement that the 1951 Trade Structure had been designed to fulfil. When the Trade Structure was modified in 1955 some of the complaints that had been raised earlier by the skilled and advanced trades were considered, and corrective measures were taken that resulted in a generally steady increase in recruiting; by 1960 it was up 50%. The intellectual standards of new recruits had gradually been raised and their technical aptitude increased to prepare them for the new breed of aircraft. To assist in utilising manpower more economically and increasing work output, work study teams had been active at RAF Binbrook and other places and produced many improvements.

To retain these high quality recruits and to compete with civilian attractions, the RAF looked inward and made its own conditions of service much more attractive than hitherto. Dining halls were redesigned and redecorated, food increased in quality and quantity, living quarters improved, rock groups were allowed and, such was the change, hair was allowed to grow a little longer! For the married airmen and

The DH Vampire, along with the Meteor, filled a vital gap in the post-war RAF fighter squadrons until the high speed interim Hunters and Javelins came into service. Both were used extensively overseas, the Vampire in this photograph belonging to No. 8 Squadron at RAF Khormaksar in 1953. The dramatic effect shown is caused by the cartridge starter giving off black smoke and spilled paraffin igniting in the jet exhaust giving off white smoke. (S. Roberts).

airwomen, much money was spent to make married quarters available without the long wait that had been the usual norm. NAAFI played its part and the Sergeants' and Corporals' Messes were places of great comfort, a process that is still maintained. Once the RAF had the recruits it ensured by keeping the standards up that they wanted to stay. Although the new airman had the opportunity to leave the service, the numbers who did were very low indeed.

The problem of continual inter-unit posting was another cause of complaint. This speciality of RAF service life must have contributed to some loss of loyalty to the service and played havoc in some marriages. Just as one had made good friends, and had become experienced on a particular type of aircraft or equipment, one could be posted — almost certainly to a completely different environment of unit or aircraft, for example from a bomber squadron to flying training school. On the other hand many men looked forward to a change of scenery as a challenge to their skills and the postings certainly provided that.

The present trade structure is a revised version of the 1964 scheme which in turn modified the 1951 structure. The 1964 scheme was designed for the smaller and more specialised needs of a high technology air force. The present one modified the existing 'ladder' system into two lists, 1 and 2, with two scales of pay (now three bands) for gradations of skill for both airmen and airwomen. Its object was to provide better prospects for the now, all-regular service, raise the technical standards for SNCOs and improve the pay and allowances. The two trade groupings are:

List 1   Mainly of aircraft trades, and including skilled trades, which give promotion by time and qualification from Junior Technician and above. Flt Sgts and WOs are promoted by selection to fill a vacancy.

List 2   Administrative and supporting trades which give promotion to NCO ranks to fill establishment vacancies. They are paid the low rate but are eligible for the high rate after 3-5 years in the rank.

With every rank subdivided into three bands the rates of pay are now similarly subdivided according to band.

One of the major benefits was that all airmen, except Flt Sgts and WOs, had to pass exams before promotion. Existing trades were reduced from 317 to 173 by combining the advanced and skilled grades of some trades and disbanding others not now considered necessary. The emphasis was on raising standards of technical knowledge, and for future SNCOs to attain the necessary standards of supervision in that trade and rank. Another benefit was the ability to earn more by passing exams to become NCOs; and another brought the supervisory ranks up to the equivalent standard of civilian life — foremen for example. Ranks were reduced from 13 to nine, those eliminated being Master Technician, Senior and Corporal Technician and the very old classification of Aircraftman Second Class. Chief Technician was retained in List 1 Trades as a link between Sergeant and Flight Sergeant.

By 1967 the effects of less money and overstretched commitments were further compounded by a drop in recruiting (from 127,000 in 1966 to 124,000) and caused the Government and the Air Staff to have a re-think about the future. It was decided to reduce overseas forces and withdraw a part into the UK. All requests for help from friendly countries would have be backed up by firmer assistance to the RAF and also the RAF would not undertake major war operations except in co-operation with allies. (With the Falklands, Britain was to be on its own but to have sympathetic non-military assistance from its friends; after that war the Falklands became a regular overseas tour for the RAF.)

The first of the major reorganisations took place within the RAF in November 1969 with the formation of Strike Command. In that process the former Bomber, Fighter and Coastal Commands became Groups. Strike Command comprised No 1 Bomber, 11 Fighter, 90 Signals and 18 Maritime Groups, the Central Reconnaissance Establishment, Military Air Traffic Organisation and the Royal Observer Corps. Strike Command was followed by the conversion of Transport Command into Support Command, and the formation of Training Command and Maintenance Command completed the UK reorganisation. Further changes were made in NATO forces by making RAF Germany a Command in its own right and a similar streamlining was carried out for the Middle East and Far East areas.

Throughout the book one of the recurring themes will be the emphasis on cost-effectiveness of various schemes and aircraft types, a constant factor in the service, particularly from 1970. Prior to that date, the effect was not as serious as it would be today, for Britain was then in a much better financial position. The reasons for the change in that position are not hard to find.

First and foremost was the change from an era of but slowly increasing inflation to the time when the oil countries suddenly increased oil prices to crippling heights, which brought about an equally crippling rise in inflation. As a result of that well-aimed blow to the West the cost of all manufactured goods rose dramatically. During the war a Spitfire cost around £9-12,000, its Meteor replacement in 1946 up to £30,000 and the American Phantom £1½M; today each Tornado costs around £15M. To put this into context, a pre-war battleship cost around £1M. The same contrasts apply to all major equipment of course; pay too went to unprecedented heights — as did the long service pensions — and the cost of training aircrew became astronomical.

The subject can only be touched on for it is not the purpose of the book, but the drive for cost-effectiveness has succeeded to a large degree in the RAF. A tradesman or woman is now trained to give a far higher output for a longer sustained period, even at the cost of increasing his comfort. All mechanical machines, from a Tornado to a station bike, are expected to give more trouble-free service, with less time on servicing or repair. It is now probably true to say that the RAF is the most efficient air force in the world for its cost.

But there still lurks the fact that the RAF is still short in manpower; the shadow of the RAF of 1933 is upon it. The experts say a next major war will be short — possibly, if a nuclear device is used. But if none is used then there is the real possibility of the NATO forces being overrun, not only by sheer weight of numbers but from sheer exhaustion of air and ground crews who will be called on to do too much because there is insufficient back-up. RAF manpower in 1981 was 88,000, all ranks, and general purpose expenditure was £1,865M.

Pay has to be competitive with civilian life to attract the best recruits, and in the 60s and 70s, with Britain's industries in almost full employment, the RAF was having to be seen to be financially attractive beyond the posed recruiting posters. Service pay is constantly under review, if not always generous, but the pay immediately after WW2 was definitely on the low side, being more akin to 1939 levels. In 1945 the daily pay for a Leading Aircraftman was:

Group A	Group B
7/6 (37½p)	7/- (35p)
Group C	Group D
6/6 (32½p)	5/- (25p)

In 1951 it was:

Regular RAF	NSA
7/- (35p)	6/6 (32½p)
NSA plus	WRAF
7/- (35p) after one year	6/9 (34p)

Extra pay was paid for specific duties outside the normal trade rates and the 1951 range was:

Qualification or Duty	Extra pay per day
Local overseas service pay	According to area
Language	2/- (10p)
Nursing (isolation and tuberculosis)	6d (2½p)
Parachutist	4/- (20p)
Parachute instructor	4/6 (22½p)
Diving	3d (1p)
Hard-lying Money	2/- (10p) Sgt and above 1/- (5p) Below Sgt
Interpreter	1/- (5p) hourly, up to 5 hours
Sanitary	6d (2½p)
Arctic	1/- (5p)
Trumpeter	3d (1p)
Flying bounty	£12 per annum

From 1 April 1954 pay was increased to come into line with civilian earnings since 1950 and, to quote the Air Member for Personnel, Sir Francis Fogarty, in a message to the airmen of the Far East Command, 'To see that skill and experience receive their award and to place a longer service career in the RAF on a firmer basis financially and thus encourage those of you who are serving on a short engagement to take on for long service'. It was Sir Francis who set in motion in the same year the Benson Experiment — and for the same reason of persuading short-term regulars to sign on for longer engagements.

The increases were for regulars only, NSA did not qualify (although the latter part of the message could apply to them) and were as follows:

J. Tech, Cpl Tech, S Tech, Ch Tech, Corporal		2/- (10p)
	Airwomen	1/6 (7½p)
AC, LAC, SAC, Sgt, Flt Sgt		3/- (15p)
	Airwomen	2/3 (12½p)
WO, Master Technician		4/- (20p)
	Airwomen	3/- (15p)

Extra pay was paid to personnel of Junior Tech and above in four trade groups; Aircraft Engineering, Radio Engineering, Armament Engineering and Electrical and Instrument Engineering. Long service pay was increased by:

After 5 years' service	Airmen	1/- (5p)
	Airwomen	9d (4p)
After 10 years' service	Airmen	2/- (10p)
	Airwomen	1/6 (7½p)

If the above figures appear ludicrously low to the present younger generation of airmen when compared with their pay today it must be borne in mind that the inflation crunch was yet to come.

On 1 April 1971 the whole system of pay was again revised by relating it to degrees of recognised trade skills in civilian industry and the new rates were set high enough to allow the deduction of set weekly amounts for food and accommodation — an unprecedented step as though airmen were living in hostels rather than messes. Continuing the civilian analogy, the whole of the pay was subject to income tax and earnings-related National Insurance at source. For this scheme all the RAF trades were graded into three bands and each band was given a pay scale. The example of a Leading Aircraftman of Band 1 on a six-year engagement in 1971, with 1985 as a comparison for inflation, is given to show the near runaway increase:

	1971	1985
Pay	£20.65 per week	£103.88 per week
Food	£2.54 per week	£15.54 per week
Accommodation	£2.19 per week	£7.50 per week

On average the pay was (and is) competitive with civilian life and in addition airmen are allowed four free railway warrants per year. Leave is generous, at least 30 days per year. The charging of fixed rates from their pay made more money available to give a wider choice of dishes at every meal and may have influenced the decor of messes and dining halls.

The total cost of airmen's pay fluctuated during the years 1948/49 (£30M) to 1969/70 (£80M) when it accelerated under the impact of inflation; £120M in 1970/71 to £243M in 1973/74. An airman's pay is now paid on a monthly basis into the bank of his choice, sealed and with details of the computer calculation, which came into use in November 1983. Another saving in administrative cost.

Chapter 2
Training for Efficiency

Despite all the technological advances in weaponry over the ages, when the crunch comes with a fighting service the successful use of that sophistication depends ultimately on the quality of the manpower. From the first shaggy-haired Neanderthal wielding a Club Mk 7, tribal, for the use of; through an archer with his Bow, Long Mk 2E, anti-cavalry; a foot of the line, firing his musket; an RFC mechanic swinging an SE 5A propeller; to a pilot flying a Tornado GR 1, nuclear bomb carrier, the country has depended on this quality, which has served Britain well.

Now it is the machine age and machine and man are more complementary than ever. Which means, very generally, that he who can operate his particular machine more quickly and efficiently in war than his opposite number will be the winner. That depends on a more comprehensive training in his skills with a deeper understanding of his psychological make-up, or exact fitting of the square man in the square hole during technical training so far as tradesmen are concerned. To this end, the standards of technical training have been continually uprated and updated, to be in line with present and future trends. That this policy is succeeding is indicated by the number of nations who have adopted similar training, or who send their own nationals for RAF training or request RAF instruction for their own air forces.

However brilliant and brave, no Chief can fight without his Indians and they usually fight according to the Chief's qualities. But between present-day Chiefs and their Indians stands a large organisation known as Training Command, which ensures that the right type of Indian is turned out. The ultimate product is a man or woman who can obey, but not blindly, can think and show initiative, is intelligent in the normal sense,

can take over command and, through all this, have a high regard for his job, service and country. The last may sound rather hackneyed but it still persists among the volunteers.

The trades available, as a glance at the 22 Trade Groups on page 19 show, are comprehensive and wide-ranging. A few of the SNCOs serving today had their initial technical training under pre-war schemes and were subsequently aligned by later courses. All of them have the know-how that comes with practical experience and which has moulded them into potential Chiefs themselves (no pun intended).

But the first step on the long road is at a Recruit School, an experience that all service men and women of all ranks are required to undergo for the necessary purpose of learning the meaning of discipline, both in the accepting and in the instilling — important in military service. The first weeks on the square under the penetrating eye and raucous commands of the drill instructor, surrounded by shouted commands, the stamping of feet and thud of rifle butts can be traumatic to some, enjoyable to others — all a matter of temperament.

A number of ex-servicemen have gone on record about their treatment at the hands of brutal, bullying drill sergeants who used the most foul language and subjected them to degrading and humiliating experiences. Even a few films have been made on this theme. So the fact that these men existed must be accepted; but so also must the assumption that there has been very little to complain about since WW2, so far as the RAF is concerned. The use of bad language is no more or no less than is found in any large organisation in civilian life. The author has known only one drill sergeant who could qualify for the above description and then only minimally. Possibly the odd one may slip through the net but the RAF will quietly remove such a man very quickly.

On the drill square, the drill instructors are usually Administrative Corporals specialising in recruit training, who are doing the job because they want to and are rewarded at the end of each course by the sight of their 20-odd former shambling, callow, disorientated youths marching effortlessly and smartly past the saluting base on the Passing Out Parade.

Between those two stages of before and after, a lot of energy has been expended, both on and off the square, in drill, physical training (PT), sport, polishing and blancoing, hut cleaning, yes and 'bull', but not of the humiliating kind, and lectures on hygiene, conduct and the history of the RAF. By about the half-way mark on the course, the recruits are usually beginning to enjoy these hectic 'live-to-the-minute' weeks. To feel genuine sorrow at leaving fellow recruits, the disbanding of the squad, seems a natural reaction.

A late volunteer, Hostilities Only, who volunteered for aircrew in 1945 was AC Ken Box, but the war was over and aircrew were being made redundant. As was the practice during this period, he was given a choice of suitable available trades: first radar operator, but he was found to be colour blind, and then airframe mechanic! Well, 'a rigger seemed more professional'.

But first he was required to do his recruit training, ten weeks at RAF Melksham from September 1945, and just to give it a bit of spice AC Box was billeted in a hut with two English lads, two from Belfast and 22 Southern Irishmen, which made life distinctly interesting. That life started at 0730 on a cold, wet and sleeting morning in September, clad in PT vest, shorts, socks and boots, running around the perimeter of a field with rifle held aloft. So it couldn't get worse! Could it?

One surprising fact emerges from AC Box's recruit training. 'Each drill routine had to be learned so that we could carry it out without orders, then all added together gradually so that on Passing Out Parade we could complete a 20-minute routine without a single word of command.' This seems to have pre-dated a form of exhibition drill which became very popular with the public some years later. Fatigues being a fact of service life, it wasn't long before AC Box was doing his share — but in the Sgts Mess, and with a difference. 'My best experience was serving food in the Sergeants Mess — fat beef, mashed potatoes and cabbage (what kind of cook was this?). After our fatigue work we were given the choice of eggs, mince, bacon or ham with chips, followed by tinned fruit and a large mug of golden brown tea — maybe I should have chosen to be a cook after all.'

All good things come to an end and after a successful Passing Out Parade when, as always seemed to amaze recruits, 'our Sergeants and Corporals suddenly became human', AC Box was posted to St. Athan for an airframe mechanics course.

The WAAF recruits' school shared RAF Wilmslow, Cheshire, with airmen, although confined to a different part of the station. First impressions were probably most striking! If not, they were going to be to girls unaccustomed to the coarser life of the service, so much so that some of the more emotional girls had the odd weep until, with the help of new-found friends, they settled down and found that the life was nowhere near as bad as it first appeared.

The accommodation was the standard wood hut, furnished with bedside lockers, wire beds with three 'biscuit' mattresses, two tables and forms and underbed lockers. As for all RAF recruits, the blankets and sheets had to be folded in an exact oblong with a blanket folded around the outside. For heating — but only when it was really cold — the hut had two 'black horrors', large stoves upon which the girls detailed vented their polishing spleen.

On arrival, the girls went through much the same procedures as the men but, perhaps naturally, felt the change from civilian clothes to service much more; they were used to lighter, feminine wear. 'The overcoat felt very heavy and the peaked cap altered many a hair style.' Regarding this latter, there is a story

Station Warrant Officer Bill Bond one of RAF Halton's most well known figures, carries out a room inspection at the Apprentice School in 1946.

(Jim Hughes)

from those days that the WAAF had the use of old steel helmets to wear under the showers to prevent their hair styles being ruined! 'Our shoes felt big, clumsy and weighed a ton.' So might have the tin hat! Everything in 1948 was primitive, a separate ablutions, little hot water and plenty of fatigues, for which thoughtful authority had issued overalls to the girls. The tin room had no sex discrimination, all were welcome, and most attended. ACW Gwyneth James, when on Fire Picquet on a Saturday, found the water hot but 'when soaking in the bath I was called out for a practice fire alarm. I had to sprint sharply to our assembly point half dry and half dressed.'

The effects of being confined, sharing the same discomforts and squad drill, were soon made apparent when 20-odd strangers became friends, united by the common bond. Most of the girls had similar experiences to the men; they actually began to enjoy the life and, when the six-week course ended and they were posted, there was a real sadness at the partings. At Wilmslow most of them left their girlhood behind and gained maturity and a sense of responsibility.

The leave-taking on posting from the Recruit School to Technical Training School was rather more emotional than AC Roberts had anticipated. 'I experienced an emotion which, throughout almost nine and a half years, was never produced in me leaving any other station. There was a lump in my throat that felt the size of a golf ball and even while feeling "parting is such sweet sorrow" I was at the same time consciously thinking "how can I feel this way about leaving a place where almost every minute of every day was organised and regimented so severely?" I still haven't worked out the answer of that one.' And many of us who have been through the mill might agree.

Recruit training at all the Apprentice Schools was the same as at other established recruit schools, with one difference. Apprentices had to endure conditions for three years instead of three months. Just to encourage the wide-eyed innocent youngsters,

Present day WRAF single accommodation by contrast with Wilmslow, showing a far superior improvement. RAF Waddington in 1977. (MOD.)

as soon as they signed on they were issued with their kit, which by 1950 had been made to fit, and also their first webbing equipment. Then they were told the good news. No going outside the camp for the first three months, no cinema for six weeks, just half an hour in the NAAFI each evening — if all was well. In that first three months they carried out drill and normal 'bull' which in 1950 was much the same as in the 30s, modified slightly perhaps. In their dormitory, the apprentices scraped with razor blades the brooms and brushes, scraped the maker's paint off the boot-polish tin and polished the bare metal buckets and coal bins, and scrubbed the deal table. Polishing the floor each Friday was ritualistic.

Inspections occurred twice weekly and were rigorous. The equipment was laid out

WRAF trainees of No. 1 Radio School at RAF Cranwell undergoing training in field exercises 1948. (G. Pritchard.)

daily and had to be blancoed with brasses polished. To make the blankets square on the made-up bed a piece of plywood was used to give a box appearance —just as Gwyneth James and her friends had done at RAF Wilmslow.

And so the three-year course commenced. An average week went something like this and was much the same on all recruit schools.

Reveille at 0630. Room jobs to be done, bed made up, breakfast and parade at 0800 for flag hoisting and prayers.

March to the technical site for work and lectures until lunch for an hour, then a repeat of the morning until 1630. Then it was back to the billets for 'bull', ironing, cleaning and, if all was well, a NAAFI break at 1930 to 2000. At 2130 it was 'Stand by your beds'. a check to see that all were present. From that check it was undress and into bed for lights out at 2200.

Wednesday afternoon was for compulsory sport, mainly cross-country running.

Saturday was a two-hour parade followed by fatigues; after 1200 there was nowhere to go until the three months were up.

Sunday began with a leisurely breakfast (by comparison), followed by a church parade at 0845 and the rest of the day was free.

Every evening there was a punishment parade outside the guardroom when those on 'jankers' appeared in full marching kit for a thorough inspection, water in the water bottles included. AC Gordon Counsell says it would be most unusual if an apprentice never attended such a parade, for average punishment was around 20 days for the three years.

Sick parade was arranged to sort out the healthy: a two-mile march was required to get to the sick quarters, followed by a lengthy wait. Any still OK were marched back after treatment.

But where necessary, treatment was first class; AC Counsell was found to have a cataract cancer, had a delicate eye operation performed by a top class surgeon and was completely cured.

The trade requirement situation in 1945 was rather chaotic, caused by the imbalance which demobilisation had created. But all new recruits had a preference on whatever trades were open — and there were many — subject to their suitability. The same conditions applied to the WAAF.

At this time it was envisaged that the post-war RAF, with its commitments to overseas and occupation forces, would be around 250,000 overall. To reach this figure quickly, the former Hostilies Only scheme was extended and a number, like AC Box, did engage on these terms. Like all recruits they had, quite surprisingly for the shortness of their terms, comprehensive trade courses. One of the least recognised was that of Nursing Orderly, a trade which tends to be kept in the background until it is needed, rather like the crash crews, one of whom is probably a Nursing Orderly anyway. The course in 1945 was held at the Medical Training Establishment and Depot (MTE and D) at RAF Halton and lasted eight weeks.

During that time a surprising amount of knowledge was given and absorbed, revealing that only an interested and dedicated person would be suitable for this trade, or really profession, as in civilian nursing. The essential Latin had to be learned and among the other subjects covered were anatomy, physiology, first aid, instruments, operating, bandaging, bedmaking using four methods (ordinary, fever, fracture and amputation), childbirth, care of the dead, VD and its treatment, instruction on hypodermic syringes and their application.

Time was spent in the School of Hygiene and Tropical Diseases and practical work was given on the building and location of latrines and wash-houses when under field conditions. At the end of this course, as in others, a passing out exam was taken and on the successful completion the new Nursing Orderlies were marched to the stores and issued with their collar dogs (or badges), a Red Cross armband and a Geneva

Convention card which certified the holder was a non-combatant. There was one peculiar and not so pleasant aspect on Course 711, which AC R. D. Quilter was attending, but it was one which tended to be rather typical at the time. Redundant aircrew were on the course and, to quote AC Quilter, 'they were Nursing Orderlies on passing the course but still retained their rank . . . Most of them . . . became instructors.' Situations of this kind had occurred mainly with the RAF Regiment. AC Quilter was posted to No.3 MT Company at Leicester.

In the technical schools many of the wartime syllabuses were modified to align with peacetime requirements, but training was still geared to the then perceived standards of technological needs; schools were later re-sited to bring Training Command into a much more efficient and compact group. In January 1946 there were only 1273 instructors against an establishment for 1664. In fact the aim was for a teaching ratio of 1:10, which would require about 2496, so already one problem was presenting itself. This showed immediately in the case of No.2 School of Technical Training at RAF Hereford, which was formed on 1 October 1945 to train Flight Mechanic Engines (probably NSA). Many were so trained, but the conditions were not of the best. The school's peak strength was in May 1946 with 3261 trainees and 350 staff. There was a severe shortage of skilled instructors, the accommodation was poor, comprising dispersed sites up to two miles away from the schoolrooms, each site with communal washing, bathing, messing and a NAAFI. Hot water was in short supply. In the winter the sites were very muddy and because of this and a wet winter there was an influenza epidemic to cope with. Lecture rooms were inadequate, with insufficient books and equipment, which contributed to a comparatively high failure rate, but this initial inadequacy of facilities was improved by early 1946. However, other factors were deemed to contribute to the general low morale besides the accommodation and colds which were presumed to have dulled the senses of the trainees. Among these were overcrowding of classes, causing stress on the instructors, and poor maintenance of the school plant and equipment, particularly electrical maintenance; during one period there was no electrician available. The staff were very concerned by the inadequate numbers of married quarters and lack of outside housing available to them. Finally, it was found that the standard of education of the trainees was low.

The school eventually found the balance and by sheer hard work in the face of these problems managed to maintain a reasonable flow of adequately trained men. But it was never a satisfactory result. In the Conclusion section of a report high praise was given to the Engineer Officers, but none for the pay clerks who had prepared the hundreds of pay packets each week; the instructors who were required to work on at wartime pace; the barrack stores continually trying to improve the dilapidated sites and replace out of date and damaged equipment; the sick bay staff who kept the hundreds of trainees generally healthy despite conditions more conducive to ill health; and none for the cookhouse staff who, constrained by the current ration allowance, probably prepared below standard meals with menus which, if introduced in today's lush dining halls cum restaurants, would probably send recruiting figures down to zero. There were no comments on the men's conditions, what had been done to alleviate them, how the instructors had coped with trainees low in morale, how the sites had been improved, if at all, what the percentage rates of passes were by entries and how the teaching aids had been improved.

The school staff, from ACH (GD) to SWO and WO Engineer, had made the school function against a background of 'the war is over' euphoria, and an understandable relaxation of effort by some whose demob number was coming up. Neither of these causes seems to have been taken into consideration. This report has been given in detail to illustrate one of the problems facing the builders of the post-war RAF.

The catering at some training schools of this time was really not very good, particularly if compared to today's standards. Most stations away from schools still had large manpower establishments and, to maintain some form of control and contentment, each station had a Messing Committee at which volunteers, or pressed men, supposedly represented their units at monthly meetings. As may be guessed, the sort of comments to be made would, if allowed, have given the cookhouse staff hot flushes, but the presence of the Catering Officer i/c Messing Committee kept that wish under control. But for all that, some of the extracts from the Messing Book of RAF Kinloss in 1949-50 are revealing and humorous and have been left to posterity and the edification of today's airmen. The following short selection has been included as typical of them all:

'The catering officer revealed that a search of the huts in the training wing and signals had produced 105 plates which were raked from under the huts (19.3.49).

The bolt referred to was one which had become loose on the underside of the mixing machine and was baked in a bun issued for tea. This type of accident happens in the best-run establishments (27.7.49).

Cold boiled ham was requested for Sunday tea. It was explained the ration did not allow for this (12.8.49).

Complaint that a number of airmen did not like kippers — it is not the function of a catering department serving from a published menu to pander to the tastes of individuals. Kippers are a welcome dish, and a pleasant change once a week (22.11.49).

A request was made for more rabbit (15.2.50).

Milk is still heavily diluted. Sgt Watkins stated that 25 gallons of milk were purchased daily whereas 50 gallons were required (13.6.50).

The bread and water supplied on the tables at the time of the inspection by

Airframe mechanics under training at RAF St. Athan in 1958, using the school Hunter.
(RAF St. Athan.)

the AOC was appreciated, but this desirable adjunct to a meal has not been repeated since. Sgt Watkins stated that he had not the labour to provide niceties of this kind as a regular thing (6.7.50). Tripe was not liked generally, and it was complained that no alternatives were served when this meal was put on (1.12.50).

The standards of catering were improved as part of the drive to increase recruiting until today when the modern RAF cooks are now winning awards in top-class competitions.

The airframe mechanics course at St. Athan in 1946 was for 18 weeks but, before his particular entry could be formed and start, AC Box spent some time in the airmen's mess tin room in the company of a WAAF of rather bad language and dubious character. Not a typical example.

The course went through a basic fitting phase, aircraft familiarisation and practical bench work, followed by Theory of Flight. Much practical work was given on basic handling of aircraft, 'tarmac sport', taxying, marshalling, starting aircraft procedures, night marshalling, refuelling techniques, and all the ramifications of operating and servicing aircraft. They were also taught basic metal repairs, paint spraying and doping and, importantly, the methods of pnuematic, hydraulic and electrical operation of flaps and undercarriages. Even cable splicing was taught. The full mechanics course, of which this was as comprehensive as any to be given to men who would spend only three years in the service, indicated the RAF's belief in thorough training. Added to this were the extra-mural activities of drill, rifle practice and PT sessions. After a last phase on automatic de-icing, chemical application (Kilfrost) and a review of general life on a squadron, the end of the course was in sight.

To preserve an in-bred smartness Ken Box and friend made the odd excursion into Cardiff where they found a Chinese laundry who did such a splendid job on their detachable RAF collars at 2½d (1p) each that they could be kept clean for three days by wiping the highly polished surface. Finally AC Box passed out successfully and was posted to his first operational unit, 138 Squadron at Tuddenham, in May 1946.

One of the largest and most efficiently-run establishments which most people hope to stay away from is a hospital. The RAF had a number during the war and retained a few afterwards, one of them being at Ely, Cambridgeshire. To this well-equipped hospital went LAC Quilter in 1947. After 3

Engine fitters removing a Rolls-Royce Derwent 5 from a Gloster Meteor F4 at RAF St. Athan, the mobile crane being typical of late and post World War 2 equipment – made to last and hard work to operate. The Meteor, along with the Vampire, was the first jet fighter into the RAF, with No. 616 Squadron, and served with distinction against the flying bombs. The aircraft was used in various roles until it was replaced by Javelins and Hunters. (RAF, St. Athan).

Bomb armourers under training at RAF St. Athan being taught bomb fusing. About 1960. (RAF St. Athan.)

MT Company cameraderie the discipline at Ely was strictly of the 'bull' kind but conditions altered for the better when a replacement CO, an Adjutant and a SWO were posted in. LAC Quilter's first work was on the wards attending to the care and comfort of patients which had to be scrupulous in the doing, or the Nursing Orderly would be in serious trouble. The same standards were applied by the RAF to curing its personnel as to its aircraft.

The work was of long hours with a shift system and just one half-day off a week and included a month of night work with no time off, but at the end of that month a four-day pass was given. Sometimes the Orderly would be in sole charge of two wards and on one memorable night LAC Quilter was acting supervisor for a large section of the hospital. On obtaining permission from the particular surgeon the Nursing Orderlies could watch operations being done: a mind-boggling occupation, but after a while very interesting. LAC Quilter recalls the number of 'splinter' trades from Nursing Orderly in his day. 'By going on further courses there were Pathological Laboratory Assistant, Operating Room Assistant, Radiography Assistant, Burns Orderly, Special Treatment Orderly (VD), Pharmacists, Nursing Orderlies who were also engaged on Air Ambulances, Air Sea Rescue and Mountain Rescue work'. All this ensured that the standard, if not the long engagement, was there and must have been of great value when the airman returned to civilian life.

Today's equivalent to the above is still varied, if different in content. They are now given rather longer names in accordance with present practice: Environmental Health Technician, Operating Theatre Technician, Electrophysiological Technician, Laboratory Technician, Radiographer, Physiotherapist, Mental Nurse, Medical Assistant and State Enrolled Nurse. Whatever their titles they all uphold a tradition on which many a sick or wounded serviceman has depended — gratefully.

When RAF technical training is made a subject of conversation then, standing first and foremost is that of the Apprentice School at RAF Halton, home of 'Trenchard's Brats' as they are affectionately known. It is to them that the RAF relies for continuity of world class standards of technical ability. From their beginning in 1920 the apprentices have continued to raise the standards until their qualities are the envy of most of the world's air forces. Essentially, all technical training schools have a high standard of training, but the apprentice has long been the elite tradesman. However, with the advent of high technology electronics and electrics, systems engineering, modern communications and superior armaments, the emphasis has shifted from the aircraft engineering trades.

In a service as small as the RAF has become as a result of various political decisions, these qualities have been invaluable to service and country. The standard of entry is very high, the training tough but superb, for these are the technical elite from whom most of the future senior NCOs — and many technical officers — will be drawn. In the early years of apprentice recruiting an entrance exam was sat at nominated towns and cities, and many of the candidates were recommended by their school with an accompanying report from the Headmaster. The first original qualification of the scheme included the statement that 'Only boys should be nominated who, in the opinion of their Local Education Authority, are suitable in character, are able to undertake the entrance examination and possess the energy, keenness and initiative essential to a successful career in the Royal Air Force'. Today's apprentices are still required to follow that precept, but instead of group sitting at a nominated place the boy will have obtained the necessary educational qualifications before presenting himself at the Careers Office.

The requirements for an apprentice Air Radio Fitter in 1950 were severe and when the apprentices began their technical training at RAF Cranwell they saw the need for the compulsory subjects of English, maths and a science subject, plus a sound knowledge of general school subjects. After a year, practical work with equipment was begun and included all the types of transmitters, receivers and communication systems in service. The various types of radar such as Rebecca and Decca Loran were taught along with IFF, interceptor and anti-submarine airborne radar, and survival equipment that utilised radio and radar. The range of equipment was wide, the variety comprehensive and the standard of teaching high.

Two years into the course No.1 Radio School was moved to RAF Locking near Bristol, a hutted camp. AA Counsell's last year as a senior apprentice was easier and the

A class under instruction at No. 1 Radio School, RAF Locking, 1984. The Senior Aircraftman at front gives visual proof of what prowess can be attained in today's RAF. (RAF Locking).

emphasis was on technical work. But even the longest courses end and passing out arrived in a flurry of exams and a final parade to which all parents of the entry were invited. Brand-new Junior Technician Counsell admitted to some embarrassment at his parents watching him on the passing out parade, but probably most lads were the same at that age. Now it was time to enter the Royal Air Force.

It is to be expected that life in the RAF must be hard at times. In a fighting service that is axiomatic, despite all the trappings of comfort and social enjoyment that the RAF has accumulated on its stations. Many exercises are designed to harden up all ranks unaccustomed to infantry-style life, priority being given to ground defence training schemes. But skill at arms is also practised and all airmen have to undergo regular ground combat training, toughening exercises and weapon training. In the early post-war years the majority of tradesmen had been trained to do technical work, with drill and arms training as a decidedly secondary occupation. They were employed full-time (and often overtime) and there was little time for exercises in infantry tactics. It is certain that Chiefie would never get the required aircraft so consistently if a proportion of his skilled men were continually detailed for defence posts each day.

The war had given tragic reminder of the

need for erks to be fully weapon trained, with exercises in their tactical use in defensive situations, i.e. defence of their airfields. The desert campaigns and Greece, Crete and Burma all saw airfields overrun by an enemy who brushed aside with ease airmen who had last fired a rifle in recruit school, and had never handled a Sten or a grenade. Their courage was not enough. From these lessons a Ground Combat Course was instituted. Little of tactics was taught despite the glaring lessons. On most of the airfields in the battle areas some airmen were taught to man light machine guns for emergency defence and low-level attack and some had time to become more conversant with arms than they had originally been taught at recruit school. Ground crew losses in WW2 were high, 16,000 killed and wounded, 4,500 made prisoner. Many of these casualties were in the great desert battles, the Burmese hinterland and Singapore. Many were trapped on their airfields by encircling movements of the enemy, with inadequate training and equipment to stand and fight or insufficient transport and knowledge to get clear, with inevitable results. Many capable and far-sighted officers and men foresaw the need for

a form of abbreviated infantry training to combat this danger and the Air Staff heeded the lessons. The RAF Regiment was formed, but by the time it was sending out trained squadrons the Allies were on the attack and the Regiment did little airfield defence, being used as light forward or holding troops — except in Greece, where they gave a good account of themselves against the ELAS.

When GCT was introduced as part of the post-war training in 1947 its aim was, to quote an extract from General Service Training Notes of that year, that:

1. All personnel should be individually proficient in the use of weapons and in elementary fieldcraft and tactics.
2. Officers, aircrew and NCOs must, in addition, be capable of commanding and leading their airmen in a battle situation and therefore must be given the opportunities of exercising leadership during their normal peace-time training.

Initially, the course was in two parts, the first mainly a weapons exercise, organised by station personnel usually from the SWO's office. a more comprehensive second part

The Hawker Hunter was, together with the Javelin, an interim fighter between the Meteor and Vampire and the supersonic Lightning and Phantom. It was introduced into the RAF in July 1954 and was a most successful aircraft, over 1,000 being supplied. The Hunter incorporated a number of advanced ideas, one of which is seen in this photograph of a No. 20 Squadron F4 version undergoing a rapid turnround at RAF Tengah, that being a detachable gunpack which helped to reduce turnround time to 7 minutes. The co-ordinated team work shown here did the rest. (Bruce Robertson Collection.

The introduction of the English Electric Lightning began the era of truly supersonic missile armed fighters. This F3 of No. 74 Squadron is being re-armed with HS Firestreak infra-red seeking missiles fitted with 50lb (22kg) HE warhead. The type entered RAF service in 1963.
(Bruce Robertson Collection).

having RAF Regiment NCOs as instructors. But due to the acute shortage of Regiment NCOs, several regional stations were made the site of a three-day course in which not only weapons and ground service training was given, but also gas mask experience and lectures in atomic (nuclear) and bacteriological warfare. RAF Hawarden was such a one and here the course consisted of a modified assault course, grenade throwing, rifle and Sten firing, and gas mask drill in a gas chamber as described above. Some tactical defence lessons were given.

In 1947 bayonet practice was still included in the syllabus for station GCT training along with the standard 25 yd (30 metre) rifle and pistol range, and indoor miniature .22 range, a battle agility course (actually a modified assault course) and, supposedly, a contour model of the station — which many never saw.

As time passed and the RAF built up its commitment to NATO, its attitude to ground defence was influenced not only by possible European involvement in a hot war, but also by the experiences of Malaya, Kenya and Aden. The European theatre was for a long time influenced by the nuclear deterrent, some thinking as a result that airfield defence would not be of much use against the BOMB; the development of a so-called battlefield nuclear device seems to make that thinking correct.

Up until at least 1957, Ground Combat Training (GCT) was a requirement that was done more in the spirit than to the letter of the syllabus. To the RAF, GCT never seemed to attain the importance it merited. A whole set of lessons needed to be taught and GCT incorporated a number of them. But in essence, it appeared that having mandatorily passed through the course, that was it: relegate it in the same way as had been done in the case of the first range-firing exercises of pre-war days.

The 1960 syllabus of Ground Defence Training (GDT), as it was re-titled, was taught at RAF Dishforth and was comprehensive. In an effort to save time lost by having WOs and SNCOs from various stations all together on a course, a typed précis was given to the named participants to study before they attended a one-day course. No instruction was given on the précis subjects, but the students were required to pass an exam before they were deemed competent (on these subjects) for another year. The subjects covered nuclear explosions, and their character and effect, radioactivity, medical aspects of nuclear warfare, fire fighting with basic rescue and first aid. All subjects were treated in detail. After 24 years, while the effects of this kind of attack will be the same, the protection and first aid will have improved. The NBC protection suits in Germany are an example. Now, the modern airmen's GDT is incorporated into his recruit training and, in addition, there are a number of tough field exercises in which he is expected to participate.

Cpl Honeybone (later WO, BEM) was sent on a Junior NCOs Course at RAF Cosford in August 1950 to train him for future promotion to SNCO, a necessary requirement. This course was a very similar version of the Junior NCOs course that the author attended at RAF Cosford in 1941. All the subjects that it was expected an NCO should know were taught in the general sense and included discipline, service documents, stores procedure, Air Council organisation, air publications, correspondence, duties, mess and catering, arrest and custody, air force law, guards and sentries, and drill. The last would be the cause of occasional chaos, for giving the orders for the first time was very different from doing them in the ranks. To those who had spent most of their time in overalls buried in a quiet corner of workshops or MT yard, being excused from parades, the impact of having to drill a large body of their fellow Corporals on a vast parade ground under the eagle eye of a drill WO could be quite traumatic. Voices which had commanded attention in the NAAFI in the evening sessions did not quite do the same on the square, and it was surprising how many of the course found it difficult to tell left from right when facing a squad.

Perhaps this might well be the place to introduce the instructor. Throughout the years, the status and quality of instructors had gradually risen until an RAF instructor is recognised as probably the best of his type in the world. A special course had been set up to teach the fine arts of instructing at No. 4 S of TT, RAF St. Athan, under the title of Organisation and Method and those who passed the rigorous and high standard of requirements, eventually became a somewhat deservedly elite group. All the latest techniques available have been introduced and not a few of these have been evolved by the school itself, from which came new ideas of relationships with the trainee, of phrasing questions correctly, of marking accurately; and all this with a leaven of psychology, which enables the instructor to assess the mental approach of the trainee. Classroom aids were introduced with modern graphics and electronics where necessary.

The school issued to its instructors, among others, a *Guide to Instructors* which was very comprehensive; many an instructor retained these Roneoed sheets when they had completed their tour. They were especially valuable where a group of NCOs might be called upon to instruct airmen, for example, of a Commonwealth air force, as in a Special Duties posting. The guide revealed the careful thought that had been put into that fine art, and shows some of the depth of the original RAF course in 1953 at RAF Spitalgate; a brief description illustrates some of the finer points and shows why the RAF instructor is of such high calibre.

Preparation and introduction of a lesson was given with its development, types of illustrations and effect of instruction on all the senses, even down to taste and smell. An instructor's speech style is analysed and the way shown to use the voice effectively to eliminate its defects. Principles of teaching were detailed — diagrams, demonstrations, class control, questioning and so on. The art of instucting has developed even further since the brief summary given overleaf:

This photograph shows the Merlin 35 of a Boulton Paul Balliol T2 of No. 7 FTS RAF Cottesmore being started by the starter trolley accumulator method in 1953.
(C. C. H. Cole).

Training syllabus
Lesson preparation
Lesson assessment
Principles of instruction
   Intelligence
   Memory and learning
Class management
Note taking
Précis
Supervision of instructors
Training aids
   Objects and components
   Blackboard
   Models
   Optics
Examination methods
   Multiple choice questions
Trade standards and trade testing
Function of Training HQ
Programme planning

The same high standard is maintained for all schools of training and in all trades and contributes materially to the consistent high standard of the average RAF airman and airwoman. It is a far cry from the pre-war methods when the trainee had to copy

A mobile classroom on display to the public in 1955. This is the type that is used to tour units giving advanced lectures on servicing methods, in this case on Goblin jet engines. The generator for power supply is from the truck at the rear. (MOD.)

information verbatim, along with blackboard drawings, into their notebooks, which made up about 50% of their teaching.

A temporary and cheaper method of informing unit tradesmen of the latest technical advances in equipment was by literally bringing the classroom to the unit tradesmen — mobile classrooms. Displays were achieved by utilising trained NCO instructors who were given the requisite manufacturer's or Air Ministry course and who then equipped and laid out a large trailer van. Usually the vehicle was driven by a Driver MT but the NCO might be given a driving course in the handling of large articulated vehicles. Some classrooms were fitted with sleeping berths/bunks for the odd occasion when there might not be accommodation on a RAF unit. The vehicle was driven around the selected chain of stations and units using the equipment and procedures to be taught, and instruction was given to successive batches of tradesmen and women who would be sent along by the various sections. The purpose of the mobile classroom was to:

1. Demonstrate the operation, construction and servicing of new types of equipment.
2. Introduce new procedures, technical and administrative.
3. Lecture on subjects included in courses at training schools with the object of cancelling or curtailing these courses.
4. Introduce equipment peculiar to one Command (or type of unit).

A great step foward in the recognition of SNCOs as men with potential for greater authority and leadership was the introduction of a carefully compiled course to train them to develop that potential. The Air Ministry had called in, a few years earlier, one of the captains of industry, a Mr. Hooper of Schweppes, to provide a syllabus for management training as applied to the service, which was so promising that it was developed into the SNCO Man Management Course in 1957.

The course was as comprehensive as it was possible to make it and included a number of subjects that puts the successful SNCO right on a par with a manager in industry. Besides the essential ones of leadership functions and principles of management, a large part of the the course was devoted to work study, work planning and control, work measurement and critical path analysis. The remainder was in SNCO efficiency, interviewing and counselling, and the important aspects of communication and manpower accounting. Many practical exercises were given and the course was of such a high standard, with great depth of detail, that the successful SNCO would see his work back on his Flight or Section in a completely different light. It was aimed at teaching the SNCO to use his manpower with the maximum of effort and economy and to plan his workload much more efficiently than before.

Another object was to enable SNCOs to reach the same levels as civilian management and it was also an essential requirement for promotion. It is most likely that the need for the course was fostered by the ever-increasing workload on decreasing numbers of SNCOs and to ensure that the most efficient types were available in the higher ranks. There would be, and were, many occasions when a SNCO or WO would have to plan vital work entirely on his own initiative, bearing in mind what was best for the RAF. To quote a part of the introduction to the course, 'Every person appointed to a position of rank and authority in the chain of command is responsible for developing and improving his power of leadership. This can be done partly as a result of learning through experience and building on inherent qualities of character and personality. In addition, much can be gained from training; just as the performance of someone with a natural flair for games will improve under coaching, so can the "natural" leader improve his ability under guidance and instruction.' When an NCO left the service he would be considered junior and middle management potential and an asset to most firms.

But during the next couple of decades

organisation and administration teaching took a minor position. The Technicians were required to expand their expertise by gaining specialist qualifications (STQ) which were essential for exam requirements. Senior Tech Ray Honeybone volunteered for the one-year Air Ministry Aeronautical Inspection Standards (AIS) course at RAF North Coates in 1952, which was necessary in third and fourth line servicing in MUs and Aircraft Storage Units. On most of these units trained civilian staff are normally employed who are quite capable of carrying out AIS work, but there are many occasions when an RAF SNCO is required to oversee their work, or even carry out an inspection.

The full range of every possible application of AIS was given, including all relevant APs, and ranging from engineering drawings through modifications, patterns, statistical sampling, stock, defects, contractors, STIs and SIs, component inspection, quality control, repair and salvage unit procedure, aircraft categories, recording, testing, to standards room procedures and the various instrumentation used. There was a slight sting in the tail; after completing the course it was necessary to gain a minimum of one year's experience in AIS duties to complete the qualification, and that meant a posting to a MU. Ray Honeybone was posted to 390 MU at RAF Seletar on Singapore Island.

During this period of the 1960s and 1970s the emphasis had been on developing the quality of technical training to keep pace with the influx of new aircraft to the detriment of general service training, admin and org. To rectify this deficiency an updated course, the Airmen's Command School, was introduced at RAF Hereford in 1980 for general service training (GST), a modern version of the old Junior NCOs course. This course was in two parts, GST1 of two weeks for junior airmen and airwomen for promotion to Corporal, and GST2 of three weeks for corporal to sergeant.

The object of the courses is to develop potential RAF and WRAF NCOs as commanders, managers and leaders, based on the work of a Professor John Adair just as Mr

Hooper had done for the Man Management course in 1957. The use of outdoor field training exercises to check these qualities culminates in exercises which simulate a squadron in a defence situation, armed attack, ground defence, escort duties. All lessons have to be assimilated and the appreciation, planning and communication understood. Other associated subjects given include station duties, air force law, drill, sergeants mess and corporals club as applicable. Students must pass successfully to obtain promotion.

The natural, and expected, follow up to GST1 and 2 for newly promoted NCOs was to develop and improve their supervisory qualities which, in general, had also suffered during the period of intense technical progress. For this purpose a Trade Management Training (TMT) course was set up at RAF Scampton in 1982.

Surmounting the difficulty of an exercise designed to test for quality of leadership at the Airmen's Command School at RAF Hereford in 1983. (RAF Official.)

The school team comprises an Engineer Officer commanding a team of Chief Technician instructors of various specialist trades, an aircraft maintenance team of four with a three-man back-up. The three week course is designed to see how potential SNCOs will make out in supervisory capacity over lower rank tradesmen and the management of available material resources. To give a more realistic background, a flight of Hunter aircraft is utilised for practical training exercises on the line, in which each student acts as leader. With these first class aids the instructing team assess the supervisory potential. Classroom theory is utilised to stimulate discussion and thinking; syndicates of four students range over the subjects of APs, orders and instructions, fire regulations, material research and the assessment of priorities, logical thought and discussion, along with presentation of their findings in correct speech and writing.

Each student is required to complete the course successfully as a prerequisite for promotion. Those that cannot make it are sent back to their units, with further hope much impaired. To bring a commonality of purpose to all, a package is given to each student on commencement of the course that contains engineering orders and instructions, engineering support services, MOD engineering staff and APs common to all trades. And not a boot repair label, laundry list or barrack damage form in sight! Such is progress.

Before all these training schemes could be instituted and bring to fruition the long term development there was first the small problem of confrontation with a former ally to begin what was to be known as the 'cold war'. Along with a number of crises, probably hastened by the cold war, they gave the necessary impetus to the Air Staff's determination to make the RAF the most efficient of forces, in spite of being starved of cash and encouragement.

Chapter 3
Cold War Confrontation

Occupied Germany was virtually at a standstill in 1945, her major industrial cities in ruins, her people workless and starving, and with many homeless; not the best of conditions for them or the four major Allies in occupation. Despite rapid demobilisation a strong air force was retained in the shape of Second Tactical Air Force (2TAF), which had been instumental in the final defeat of Germany, as part of the British Forces of Occupation (BAFO) formed in July 1945 This decision turned out to be wise in the long term, as 1948 was to show. No. 80 Squadron, 2TAF, was operating Tempests at RAF Wunstorf and to this squadron LAC Box brought his newly-won talents as an Airframe Fitter in May 1947.

He had travelled by ferry from Hull and en route to Wunstorf had seen the sorrowful aftermath of war as it affected children in the bombed devastation of their towns. Wunstorf was an ex-Luftwaffe station and airmen's quarters were a considerable improvement on the UK; two men per room, each with a wardrobe and a mat, good heating and double glazing. There were even bedsheets!

Box's first job as a fitter was to change a rudder, helped by the Airframe Sgt of B Flight, who apparently had been lying in wait for him. The squadron was a mobile unit and was on 24-hour standby, which meant that as many aircraft as possible should always be serviceable. A Tempest was quite a good test of a fitter's ability, requiring much fitting and removing of long range tanks and rocket rails, undercarriage snags and for the engine men the delight of a buried engine installation. Flying was intensive with emphasis on the aircraft's speciality of ground attack using rockets. The armourers were still busy in their recent wartime role.

To give the squadron practice in mobility it was sent to RAF Gatow in Berlin and while

there, on show to the French, Americans and Russians, the squadron intensified both its flying and its 'bull'. At Wunstorf guard duties were undertaken along with billet inspections, rifle firing and general drill sessions. On one occasion the squadron was sent to Mengen on a joint exercise with the French Air Force, and on another occasion the squadron had a short detachment to RAF Duxford for the 1948 Battle of Britain fly past followed by rocket firing demonstrations on Salisbury Plain from RAF Middle Wallop.

Off duty, LAC Box saw as much of the country as possible and in the process quickly learned quite a lot of the more blatant facts of life that existed in occupied Germany. He learned who was hungry, the value of good friends and of cigarettes, the 'free and easy' way of life. In Berlin at that time there was no Checkpoint Charlie; it was quite easy to go into the Eastern Sector, provided you left by 2100 hours, and one could still shake hands with a Russian soldier.

Life on 80 Squadron was fair rehearsal for the intensive work that was to follow on all NATO squadrons. Despite six years of a fearsome conflict there was still the possibility of a flare-up in Europe, and one such incident on the Yugoslav border had the mobile unit on standby, which meant a lot of packing in a hurry. Also, it being Occupied Germany, armed guards were considered necessary: always a good way of absorbing any spare time the erks might have. As Ken Box remarked, 'there was a very different "feel" about squadron life in Germany — much more activity — certainly more involvement of higher authority — as if the war was still on. Maybe there were other reasons that ground crew knew nothing of — I'm sure there were'. Which is fair comment.

The Berlin Airlift, which started in June 1948, was not strictly a brush war but an example of a kind of operation that had first originated at Kabul in Afganistan in 1929. It was also the first definite indication of Russia's attitude to her former allies and to post-war Europe, a guideline to the ruthless application of her policies and a pointer to the cold war to come. The Korean airliner shot down by them over Sakhalin Island in September 1983 indicates that her policy still remains as ruthless.

The Kabul airlift was for people, 585 of whom were brought out in the old biplanes, the ground crew working from such places as Kohat and Peshawar; for Berlin it was the very necessities of life that were flown into the beleagured city from satellite airfields. The operation was a tripartite Allied effort and the first cold war confrontation with their former ally. To all ranks, men and women who carried out the actual work, it was to be an operation of major war intensity but without the bombs and bullets. Aircrew were to be flying as intensely as in war but in transports instead of bombers, and without their dedication the airlift would have failed. A multi-national administration controlled the servicemen and civilians, British and German, French and American, who got down to the physical work of keeping the whole operation going. Everyone, from the top of the Command pyramid down, did a first-class job in his particular sphere; here we are concerned with the airmen.

The first major problem to overcome was the chronic shortage of skilled ground tradesmen and air transports, both vital requirements. The Malaya emergency had begun just a month before and the Far East Command was being supplied by Transport Command, while the WW2 demob effect was still being felt in the shortage of skilled regulars. It was a case for drastic measures and all large air transports on the run to Malaya were diverted to Germany. The UK

German civilian workers enlarging the tarmac area at RAF Wunstorf in 1948 during the Berlin Airlift, or Operation Plainfare. HP Hastings are at rear. (RAF Official.)

was combed to find skilled tradesmen who were posted to the airfields in use, including volunteers for a six-month detachment to RAF Wunstorf. The transport squadrons sent their own detachments to the same airfields.

There were, as may be expected, many teething problems; aircraft handling, communications, feeding and sleeping the aircrews and handling staff, loading and unloading the aircraft and MT, and of course, the split-second timing of aircraft operation that became such a feature of the airlift. During the operation several Air Ministry Science teams carried out various investigations and their findings, so far as ground crews are concerned, makes interesting reading. Interesting too was the fact that a form of work study was being instituted so soon after the war. Their findings are given later.

For those qualified tradesmen who had volunteered for a six-month tour to help, the journey across France and Germany was a salutary one as they surveyed the devastation caused by the Allied bombing offensive. Their arrival at Wunstorf was well organised and the men were shown to the ex-Luftwaffe's barracks formerly occupied by LAC Box and friends but now six men to a room instead of two. AC Don Leech's first impression on landing at Wunstorf was the vastness of the tarmac apron and the sight and sound of large numbers of multi-engined aircraft. One rather

Malcolm Club rest hut for ground crew of RAF Wunstorf (and a few civilians) at 0300 during the Berlin Airlift. The notice which reads, 'Guests of the RAF. Therefore conduct yourself accordingly' was observed. (Don Leech.)

good idea was to have one station airman on a bike going around with their arrival chits to all the required sections, which saved a few man-days. For some reason the unit had no squadron number — just A, B and C Flights. The hours of work were divided into three eight-hour shifts, eight hours on, 16 off.

The tradesmen went straight to work. It was a Continental winter and they were issued with cold weather clothing: 'and what with lace-up knee boots, parkas and Russian-style fur hats we looked more like Cossack cavalry than erks. Life became very hectic and very, very cold. Ice affected every job that one did and created its own job. I and other FMEs and FMAs spent lots of time on tall wooden platforms built on the rear of 15-cwt transports accompanied by German ex-POWs spraying de-icer fluid onto wings, tailplanes and tops of the Yorks' fuselages'.

All newly arrived FMEs had to prove their ability to start and ground run the aircraft and do running checks. They were required to pass this test with 'Chiefy or one of his Sgt Fitter IIEs . . . in the right-hand seat . . . My ground running experiences up to this time had been about a total of four occasions spent in the cockpit of a Spitfire, Beaufighter and Meteor at St. Athan . . . This particular operation of getting the engines warmed up saved aircrew precious time in the cabins waiting for warm up before they joined the take-off queue. We experienced, and became adept at curing, all the usual snags . . . on the Merlin XX and its ancillary equipment. Oil leaks, constant speed units, magneto drops and changes, plug harness changes, etc. Ground equipment such as steps and engine platforms were in short supply and one spent much time scouring dispersal for the necessary equipment before one could start'. If an engine's bearings were suspect the oil filters had to be dropped to check for any metal in them, an unpleasant job on a windy day. If metal was found the engine had to be changed and the aircraft went into the hangar where a team of skilled and experienced Fitter IIEs under a SNCO carried out the change. Other trades were equally organised.

'A slight indication of working conditions was when that worst enemy of flying — fog — descended and flying was cancelled, it was also a mixed blessing, for many small jobs which had been waiting for time could be done and the flight line shift could get a well-earned break after completing any snags. If all was quiet, three wooden toolboxes were quickly placed end-to-end . . . overalls rolled up to make a pillow and one got one's head down.' But time spent on the ground was less time supplying the beleaguered people of Berlin and everyone was soon fretting with impatience waiting for the fog to disperse.

Part of the social life at RAF Wunstorf, such as it was, was spent in the Malcolm Clubs of which there were two. The smaller one, more a canteen on the airfield in a Nissen hut, was always occupied, always smoky at whatever time and, in times of fog, 'a seething mass of erks . . . playing cards, epithets and ribaldry being hurled about the place and a notice over the counter informing . . . "You are guests of the Royal Air Force, please conduct yourself accordingly".' If the men went into Hannover they could see large areas of ruins, some marked with the black crosses that indicated bodies were still entombed and, in the dark winter nights of 1948/49, 'there was much scurrying and furtive meetings between BFO and the local wide boys, eager to do a deal on the black market . . .'.

Besides the Yorks there were of course the numerous aircraft of the civilian air charter firms. Wunstorf was one of the supply bases and here operated the Avro Tudors of British South American Airways, the Lancastrians of Flight Refuelling used for carrying fuel oil, civilian Yorks of Skyways and two Tudor tankers of Airflight in the capable hands of Air Vice-Marshal D. C. T. Bennett, who performed prodigies of organisation and personal involvement, even down to doing his own servicing. The civil units were eventually concentrated at Fuhlsbuttel.

As the weather improved to the warm days of May the airmen in the barracks found the site wasn't so good; they were plagued by mosquitoes, and the area became hot and dusty. But there was no time to grumble, rather to exult for the airlift was winning. Just before the Russians admitted defeat, LAC Leech flew home to attend an aircrew selection board, and passed.

Some stations worked a three, 12-hour, shift system which meant that airmen were

Part of a load for Berlin, probably grain, secured to the floor of a York transport on the Berlin Airlift, 1949. (Don Leech.)

working an average of 56 hours weekly, changing shifts at midday and midnight. A problem here was that erks, being quite normal, liked to go out to the nearest town for a break, check out the local ladies and try the brew. As a result they might crawl back into camp rather tired, not quite in the state to commence a 12-hour shift at midnight. So a further shift system of 8 hours on, 16 off, for six days, then two days off, was introduced which had the effect of reducing the average weekly hours worked to 48.

To maintain the energy output needed in a physical operation of this nature necessitated good food at all meals, and to feed the men properly required the catering staff to prepare meals throughout the day and night. No mean feat was to occur, for the staff consistently provided around five meals per man at irregular times during each 24-hour day. Just prior to the operation, codenamed Plainfare, the meat ration to the services had been reduced; Britain was still recovering from the war and was also on rations. The cuts were restored for the period of the operation and much ingenuity was shown by catering staff to make the meals attractive. To assist all ranks, a hut was placed on the tarmac areas to serve hot drinks only and was much appreciated, but not abused.

For the ground crew of the transport squadrons it was one of the great pinnacles of their achievement and they sweated blood to keep the aircraft on the routes. The British sense of humour still persisted despite all, and there is the small tale that epitomises that humour. On landing, a pilot put his aircraft unserviceable in the F700 as 'Something loose in the rear compartment'. When he came to collect the now serviceable aircraft he checked the F700 and saw against his report, 'Something tightened in the rear compartment'.

If one can imagine such a scene, the following passage is an attempt to convey the frenetic atmosphere of a night's operation. RAF Gatow had a vast concrete apron and onto this taxied an aeroplane, on average, every three minutes, which meant several aircraft could arrive in a bunch. At the turn-off point from the taxiway an airmen would direct the aircraft's pilot with torch signals, and by a succession of airmen the aircraft was marshalled to join a line, nose to tail, of fresh arrivals. In the darkness, the noise of Merlins, Hercules or Pratt & Whitneys made a suitable orchestration with flashing torches and the reflected lights of Berlin as a backdrop.

When the aircraft stopped near brightly lit hangars, gangs of civilians immediately swarmed over it, most to start unloading the flight cargo into MT which had backed up to the freight doors. First line tradesmen refuelled, checked and did their After Flight inspections, and received reports from the aircrew. Local Mrs. Mopps cleaned the interior of the aeroplanes as much as they could in the brief time available. The aircrew went off to Air Control to get briefed on the return trip, keeping an eye open in the dark for trucks. Whilst this activity was going on, the aircraft at the head of the queue was being loaded with materials manufactured in Berlin and flown out to sell. Not all the aircraft would be so loaded; some might be carrying servicemen or local citizens, some returning empty. And another queue was forming.

The lead aircraft started up, its engine noise merging with that of the arrivals. A quick full revs check, a wave to remove chocks and the aircraft was being marshalled to the exit from the apron. Before it had done so the next aircraft in line had started. The taxying phase was the most dangerous part of the operation as at times and against different lighting the turning propellers were difficult to see. Fortunately, accidents were infrequent.

This scene, full of noise, limited visibility, shouted orders and directions, vehicle movement and moving bods against light and dark shadowed background, and all the time with the sound of aircraft taking off and landing, carried on all night to leave a tired, unshaven group of men (and shaven women) to take a quick meal, gratefully seek their beds, and leave the new shift to carry on. And this went on continuously for a year.

The aircrew, too, did a fabulous job and all credit to them, flying the routes at an intensive pace in all weathers, subjecting the aircraft to stresses and strains for which they had been designed but seldom encountered and which needed first-class servicing to sustain. This was supplied by equally dedicated ground tradesmen.

The findings of the Air Ministry Science teams, mainly at RAF Gatow were: Ground crews often found it difficult to locate an aircraft at night and as the distances could be long — the flight line was up to 1000 yards (300m) — a man carrying tools and equipment might spend some time in getting to his work (as LAC Leech found). This was solved by the provision of permanent illuminated parking points and, to assist the work, electricity was laid on at these points for wandering leads. The time taken between pilots reporting defects to air control, which might be 15 minutes away, and the ground crew finding the aircraft could be too long, so the aircrew radioed any defects to air control when within 10 minutes of landing. Aircrew were also required to report directly to the aeroplane before flight and check any work, the aircraft's F700 and relevant documents. Very quickly, servicing and landing bays known as 'clutches' were marked out, each bay self-contained with tools, services, ground equipment and aircraft records and each linked to control. A local building nearby, or an erected hut, was used for storing spares to save long walks.

One special irritant was soon corrected, that of loading an aircraft, finding it unserviceable and having to unload. Another was of pilots missing their 'slots' in the line and causing obstruction. A further cause of dissatisfaction was aircraft on terminal inspections at their UK base taking up to four days for a 14-hour worktime inspection.

At the beginning of the operation MT had a tough time with a shortage of vehicles and no organisation, but after the initial small problems of shortage of manpower — loaders, drivers and mechanics — and route organisation and control had been sorted out, the MT settled down to moving the 390,000 tons of material in its usual slogging fashion. It met many problems of loading and unloading, as did the ground crews, but with

determination mastered them. The drivers saw at first hand how their efforts were being appreciated, which gave them the more incentive.

A continental winter is usually much colder than in the UK and the authorities were quick to have ready the special cold weather clothing, which ranged from windproof outer covering to snow goggles, mittens, parka and woolly underclothes. In the event, fortunately, the winter was not as severe as usual. But out on the tarmac the aircraft had to be defrosted or have snow removed and special parties were detailed to this, using the accepted Kilfrost method and wearing oilskin protective clothing, the latter very unsuitable in cold weather.

Away from the airfields Sunderlands flew from their base at Finkenwerde near Hamburg into Lake Havel in Berlin under similar extreme conditions of operation to the landplanes. Their flight control at Finkenwerde was a row of marquees and, on Lake Havel, a local yacht club was their operating, loading and unloading point. Flying boat operation is a specialised skill; taxying alone on a frequented lake with no brakes and the wind in the wrong quarter can be hazardous. Servicing these beautiful machines calls for different qualities when the boat is rocking in wash or swell, and there is no protection from the weather on a folded down leading edge. Manhandling the big boats was necessary because of the quite considerable loads they were required to carry but, despite all the natural hazards of loading and unloading on a small wharf or into barges, little damage was caused. A flying boat mechanic becomes very fond of his bulky charge. The winter ice caused their withdrawal.

The Berlin Airlift has been well recorded and in 1949 HMSO produced an excellent booklet *Berlin Airlift*, an account of the British contribution, its cause and effect, the organisation and administration, the work of the aircrew and of the German labour force. It does not describe the work done by the RAF ground crew other than a small appreciation for the work output that enabled the intensity of aircraft operation to be maintained. Little recognition is given to the erks or NCOs who beat their brains out or knackered themselves getting Dakota, Hastings, York or whatever aeroplane turned round, unloaded, reloaded where necessary, and refuelled in such a short time, MT serviced and loaded and personnel fed, bedded, paid, warmed — and doing this continuously night and day while the emergency was on.

In this operation the RAF lost men and was seriously short of manpower — to the point where most of the home Commands were seriously weakened to supply them. Overseas bases also felt the strain as transport aircraft for their supply were withdrawn and diverted to Germany.

A few statistics to close the account. The operation cost £10¼M and 75 air and ground crew were killed. The amount moved by aircraft type, in short tons, was:

York   233,000 (235.8M kg)
Dakota   101,000 (91.6M kg)
Hastings   55,000 (49.8M kg)
Sunderland   5,000 (4.5M kg)

Number of aircraft on average:

York   40
Dakota   50
Hastings 16 (from Oct. 1948 only)
Sunderland 10 (until Dec. 1948 only)

Flying hours: 150,000   Sorties: 66,000
Percentages of total effort: RAF 17%; British civilian airlines 6.3%, USAF 76.7%

The total effort was 2,325,809 short tons (3297M kg) delivered between late June 1948 and early September 1949, and included:

Coal 1,586,530 tons (1466M kg)
Wet fuel 92,282 tons (83.7M kg)
Food 538,016 tons (502.5M kg)
Export goods manufactured in Berlin 34,240 tons (29.2M kg)

The cost to Britain, excluding aircraft wear, was estimated at £5,850,000

The following is an extract from a report by General Ridgeway, US Army, Supreme Allied Commander for the year 1952-53:

'In 1952 the USSR Air Force had over 20,000 front line aircraft. Some of their equipment was better than that of NATO, whose aircraft were mainly obsolescent piston engine types and a Signal Command which was inadequate. Stocks of ammunition were low, supply and maintenance equally inadequate. There was a shortage of specialists, unbalanced supply lines. Although much progress had been made, NATO is still (1953) insufficient to give prospects of success because it is not up to strength. More pilots and ground crew are needed, together with aircraft control, warning and reporting systems.'

In the early years Germany relied for its air defence on the British Air Forces of Occupation (BAFO) until the formation of NATO in April 1949; under a reorganisation programme in September 1951 the wartime 2nd Tactical Air Force was re-formed to operate with other signatory nations' air forces. With the increased commitments Allied Air Forces Central Europe was formed. Tactical planning at first was an extension of wartime procedures but the introduction of new aircraft and their application to NATO defence meant that continual updating was required. As it became clear that NATO operations would be based on a continuous alert posture, the need for instant first strikes and the threat of the nuclear bomb, so many exercises were carried out to formulate and test tactics and the strategic thinking behind them.

To those operating the aircraft and equipment, life was at first what could be called routine squadron work. It was only when the gradual changes to a more urgent style of life began to bite, necessitated by the massive build up of the East against which their pitifully few squadrons would be committed, that a posting to a NATO unit meant that the key words would be *work* and *alertness*. More than in the UK, they would be committed to a tour that was ruled by exercises, alarms, long hours of work, shift systems; whether single or married, it made no difference. There were some perks in such a posting but they would be earned.

A posting to Germany is more than just another change of scenery — it is an unforgettable experience which to the thinking man will bring home vividly, and very personally, just why so much cash and time have been expended on his training; he will realise the potential of his air force and understand the very real danger from the Warsaw Pact (WARPAC) countries. A posting to one of the operational squadrons guarantees variety during his tour. After arrival procedures and settling down into his quarters, our erk will report to his Flight of the Hunter, Jaguar, Harrier, Phantom and Tornado squadrons where he will be issued with special kit and protective clothing. He will be shown the dispersal area and the inside of a Hardened Aircraft Shelter (HAS). He will be told his new duties — and somewhat different some of them will be. He will meet his new acquaintances (they will soon be friends). As a tradesman he will soon be asking technical questions: What, where, when, maybe why, and the basic ones like: Where's the nearest town, the beer, the local crumpet, SWO, CO, Flight Commander, Flt Sgt, and what's the NAAFI like? As an NCO he will have been put into the picture by his fellow NCOs: the SWO will soon have them all marked down for duties.

Our erk will be given time to acquaint

Aircraft weapon technicians re-arming a Phantom with AIM 9 sidewinder air-to-air missiles in a hardened aircraft shelter in RAF Germany, 1976. (MOD.)

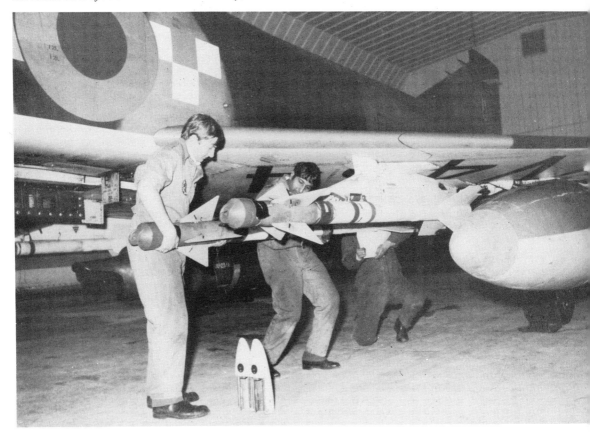

himself with the APs, SROs, DCIs, technical orders and the various sections. Soon he will be nearly ready for that duty that makes him a complete NATO type: a 24-hour stint with a fellow ground crew member on the Battle Flight in a HAS. This is a job that combines action with boredom. During their stint the two ground crew will be sited in a small room in the shelter with the duty aircrew in another. Two aircraft (one for back up) are kept in the HAS. Immediately upon landing from a sortie an aircraft is taxied into the HAS and the electrically-driven heavy steel doors closed. It is then serviced by the relevant trades, refuelled and re-armed where necessary. The aircraft faces the opposite set of doors and when all is completed and the F700 signed, the ground crew retire to their crew room and await an alarm signal. The aircrew do the same; they are all in radio communication with control. The HAS virtually requires a direct hit with a large charge weapon to be put out of action.

On an exercise (and for real) an enemy aircraft sighted on radar triggers an alarm to a Battle Flight to scramble and the ground crew dash to the aircraft, the aircrew leading by a short head as they have to get into the cockpits. The pilot is secured and is starting the engine(s) before the ground crew has got clear. The steel doors are opened and the aircraft taxies rapidly out and on to the runway for take off. Battle Flight aircraft are plugged into ground control in the HAS, the cable of which disconnects when the aeroplane taxies out.

The essential exercises of peace are to rehearse for the worst conditions of war. These include aircraft presumed to have flown through radioactive nuclear fall-out. Which means decontamination practice, performed by air mechanics or assistants in NBC suits, an exacting and warm job for anyone.

On a NATO station, the HAS are deliberately scattered haphazardly to minimize damage from air attack. There are also aircraft hides built deep in accessible woods and forests for the Harrier, all carefully camouflaged — but with everyone

highly conscious that they can be detected by heat and colour detection cameras. Ground detection is of such importance that special linescan cameras have been developed that give pictures based on the different heat emission characteristics of anything below. The RAF is so aware of this that it makes sure that the standby Battle Flight shoos away any recce aeroplanes. Not much can be done about enemy satellite observation except more efficient camouflaging. All major points on the airfield are protected by 'fortified' type defences against the possibility of Fifth Column attacks and, more than in WW2, kitchen staff, clerks, stores personnel, etc. are available and trained to use arms for defence.

A Tactical Evaluation (Taceval) exercise is designed to monitor reactions of a station when an alarm is sounded (teams from Taceval position themselves in places best suited to observe). All stations are subjected to these, which are done on an 'unwarned' basis. When the alarm sounds all personnel must get to their action stations no matter what they were doing. The exercise tests all aspects of preparing aircraft and loading with weapons and bombs. Protective clothing is worn all the time and loading 454 kg bombs in a hurry or fitting 27 kg rockets on a hot day can be distinctly uncomfortable in a NBC suit (designed to give protection in nuclear, biological and chemical warfare). All airmen are armed — training has been such that the erks are reasonably good infantry-type airmen, which in Germany is nearly as important as technical ability.

The range of functions tested is large, but within the confines of this book include: support functions, engineering and ground staff operations, ability to survive, guarding, security, fire fighting, damage control, chemical warfare drill, arming, take-off times, turnrounds. The aircrew will be tested on their own particular jobs with great emphasis on detail. Other points checked are airfield defence, cross-servicing (one tradesmen servicing other trades' equipment), medic care, intruders on the ground, attack damage and repair, dog patrols, evacuation drill, MT operations, etc.

RAF Germany's NATO stations (previously 2 Tactical Air Force) up to 1984 were at, and housed:

Rheindahlen	HQ RAF Germany and HQ 2 TAF 14, 17, 31 Squadrons (Jaguar GR Mk1) and 37 Squadron RAF Regiment
Laarbruch	15, 20 Squadrons (Tornado) 16 Squadron (Buccaneer S Mk2 B) and 26 Squadron RAF Regiment Quick Reaction Alert (Interceptor) Force QRA (1) (Lightning, Phantom)
Wildenrath	19, 92 Squadrons (Phantom FRG Mk2) 60 Squadron (Pembroke) 16 Squadron RAF Regiment Battle Flight
Gutersloh	3, 4, Squadrons (Harriers) 230 Squadron (Puma HC Mk1) 18 Squadron (Chinook HC Mk1) 63 Squadron RAF Regiment

The RAF Regiment Squadrons were mainly Rapier equipped and these are sited according to tactical requirements.

Joint membership of NATO brought variety to all ranks of the RAF; it gave most of them an opportunity to see large areas of Europe and the chance to practise a language right in the homeland; NATO service has superseded the Middle East and Far East as the main areas of overseas service. Because of the RAF's commitments, and the watchfulness required against a vastly superior force of men and machines, life on a NATO squadron is about two points short of hot war, with all that that implies: shift work, overtime, constant exercises, restricted radius of leisure and social activity. But despite the

Confirming camera operation after removing film magazine from camera installed in a PR Mosquito (mark unknown). Object on ground is a long-range overload fuel tank. About 1951.
(Bruce Robertson collection.)

ever-present possibility that the Eastern bloc armies could suddenly advance overnight, the erks are still able to live out in well-built and equipped MQs.

A vital trade in today's present confrontation is the interpretation of photographic prints from reconnaissance sorties, the interpreters usually being officers. Their units are normally within close range of the airfield from which fly the Jaguar or Phantom PR aircraft. Essential for efficiency and quick results is a first-class Photographic Reproduction Unit (PRU) such as No. 25 at Rheindahlen, which claims to be RAF Germany's oldest unit, having arrived in Germany on 31 May 1945 from its landing in Normandy just behind the initial forces, and been in continuous service ever since under its previous title of No. 4 Mobile Field Photographic Section. Under progressive development and changes of title, this unit is now one of the most organised and efficient in Western Europe, with an output of photographic and reproduction items that would make a statistician drool.

Today after a PR sortie, a Phantom or Jaguar will taxy into its dispersal and have the film unloaded from the cameras and on its way to Recce Imagery Processing Flight in less than two minutes. The Flight, if required, can develop the film at the equivalent speed of about 120,000 rolls of 35 mm film in 15

Catering staff of RAF Hullavington assembling a mobile field kitchen of the type used in NATO exercises, about 1981. (MOD.)

minutes. First film is ready in 4 minutes, a single print in 90 seconds and every 15 seconds thereafter. But if large numbers of prints of any kind are required quickly, the negative film is sent to the PRU at Rheindahlen, where the most modern machines, which cost around £1M, enable it to produce 1000 identification photos per month, up to 100,000 prints a day from operational recce film, hundreds of assorted prints in both black and white and colour each day from the multifarious activities of its large photographic staff, copier printing up to 250,000 copies a month, and overall using several tons of paper each month.

The unit gives its resident photographers much variety, which includes helping record police evidence, photographing surgeons at work and in the forensic lab (not for the squeamish) and covering all aspects of service operational and social life. The modern thirst for more and more copies to file, forget and throw away, is satisfied by a comprehensively equipped section. It is the finishing school where the RAF Photographer, Ground, can master his craft.

A little known part of the NATO border is to the far north. Operating in flying conditions, which at times bring freezing cloud, white-out and high gusting winds, can bring the fear of icing-up, which can occur in seconds. Along with the weight and mass of the ice there is the inconvenience of frosting cockpit windows and poor outside visibility to tax the pilots' skill and confidence. Helicopters are used extensively, continuously exercising for possible hot war operations in which they will be required to move troops and their equipment, such as 105 mm field guns.

Servicing of the helicopters is shared by Army and RAF and done out of doors; quite awkward, for it is not recommended in these low temperatures to touch metal with bare hands, so one must presume that servicing tasks are arranged so that this condition is minimised. A main problem to Gazelle maintenance was condensation on the electrics caused by the early morning air warming up more quickly than the aircraft

Catering staff of RAF Brize Norton, using a similar field kitchen of the type shown in the previous photograph, and which is used by NATO, during an exercise in 1977. (MOD.)

and thus causing shorting. To prevent this, the particular parts were sprayed with the service equivalent of the motorist's can of 'damp start'.

Specialist PR squadrons regularly carry out exercises in the area and, as they are also mobile units, bring everything with them, care of the Hercules of Support Command. The processing cabins are designed with this in mind and double (or treble) up as sleeping accommodation and stores containers. These cabins are known, with the modern service's penchant for American-style titles as, hold it, Air Transportable Reconnaissance Exploitation Laboratories (ATREL). When in operation the processors can produce developed, dried film of one aircraft's full recce (up to five cameras) in about eight minutes.

For all ranks an exercise may entail the wearing of NCB clothing, with its consequent restrictions on some tasks. With the squadron being self-contained and to keep its manpower to an economic minimum, the SNCOs of airframe and engine trades are sometimes called on to help out in another trade such as MT, armament or radio, providing it is within their technical capability. The biggest bugbear on servicing is the risk of frostbite and great care is taken to

keep gloves on, which requires some working practice when doing a small, delicate job. Certain parts are pre-warmed before fitting.

On the icy surfaces of runway and line area there is the occasional flap of an aeroplane sliding under braking and for this eventuality a 'chock man' is standing by to place a chock quickly under the wheels of the sliding aircraft — one of the few uses of that now discarded item. Leisure on these exercises ranges from very little to nil: it depends on the nature of the exercise how much off-duty time is allowed.

One way of keeping the men contented is good victuals, so tagging along with the squadron will be a Mobile Catering Support Unit (MCSU), trained to feed these squadrons in the field. As well as being excellent high speed cooks — a hot meal ready within three hours of being off-loaded with their equipment — the caterers have to have a technical bent because they erect and maintain their own tents, and service their own equipment, including electrical appliances and generators. For exercises of this kind they produce high calorie meals three times a day, along with hot drinks in between, and have rather more problems in defrosting food in the bitter cold within the Arctic Circle. The MCSU is probably a derivative of the Field Catering Flights that

Tempest V W2-Y of No. 80 Squadron at RAF Wunstorf, 1947/48. (K. Box.)

The spectacular sight when a Javelin F(AW) starts up on the Koffman cartridge starter about 1956. The night fighter version is similar (C. C. Cole).

have been raised for support purposes with mobile NATO squadrons. The quality of their product is such that yesterday's airmen who got his 'food' on the desert and jungle airfields of WW2 would think these cooks had been recruited from the Savoy.

The 'cold war' confrontation units are not all in Europe. Back-up and support forces are held in the UK and their training is just as severe and each year are given realism in a geographical sense by going on exercises into NATO countries. When the threat from the East was finally confirmed by the Berlin Airlift, several squadrons were attached to Second Tactical Air Force, as it then was in Germany, operating under the aegis of the UK. Early fighter squadrons operated Spitfire, Fury, Tempest and Meteor aircraft and carried on their training based on their recent wartime activities. At that time, despite the large and rapid demob of tradesmen and aircrew, the RAF still had sufficient squadrons available to man this force with some strength. Then with the compounding factors of the signing of the Warsaw Pact and the building-up of their forces, the steady rundown of the RAF and the pull out of NATO by the French, it became imperative to increase the efficiency even more. New

aircraft were coming into service with this in mind, including the Javelin and Hunter F2.

The last-named aircraft was introduced into UK squadrons in 1954 and among the first to equip were 257 and 263, previously with Meteors. In the first days the squadrons had insufficient information about them; initially there were few manufacturers' courses. So to the tradesmen it was a matter of feeling their way, and in the case of carrying out a first engine change Corporal Engine Fitter Harry Turner writes, 'We did this with the Volume I, or whatever, in one hand, spanner in the other. Consequently, we were rather slow at first . . . our team's first engine change took almost three days. After a few months we had it down to three hours, and that included engine runs.'

Starting the first Javelins and Hunters was spectacular, as they were equipped with a cartridge starter which turned the engine over by firing a large cordite cartridge in a starter that looked like a small Gatling gun. The resultant start was a drama of noise and smoke. Rarely, two cartridges fired at once, which was even noisier and expensive in repairs to the aircraft. It also frightened the life out of the fitter!

At one time, one of the new-fangled

innovations was the ejector seat. The action of seat ejection was by firing a cartridge in a special tube, triggered by a cable attached to a face blind which the pilot activated by pulling the blind over his face. To prevent a few serious accidents that had occurred with the seat being accidentally fired during ground servicing, a safety pin was provided. In the early days this was fitted by a tradesman when the aircraft had stopped, and removed just before taxying away. Harry Turner had 'a touch of the frighteners' when fitting a seat with the help of an Assistant. While fitting the seat, Turner got it slightly trapped and asked the Assistant to raise the seat slightly, which he did, 'but just too far and the barostat tripped (for setting the parachute release from the seat); it ticked very rapidly, urgently and loudly, and I did the mid-air running thing, much to the amusement of my armourer mate who was waiting to put the seat cartridge in . . . .'.

After a pilot was prematurely ejected as a result of incorrect seat fitting by a non-armament tradesman, and his Hunter entered a haystack at near supersonic speed, the job of fitting ejector seats and safety pins was left to armourers.

Because of the Public Relations glamour of these new aircraft and the way they had captured public imagination, an At Home display was held at RAF Wymeswold in 1956. Corporal Turner was minder to a Shuttleworth 1910 Deperdussin. He said that after six hours of 'They've come a long way in 40 years' and similar profound comments he was rather cheesed at the end of the day.

All the basic techniques of rescue from aircraft were honed on the operational stations of WW2, both home and overseas, during terrible nights when flak-damaged aeroplanes crash landed, often with fatal results. Many people owed their lives to the teamwork and dedication of erks who were only rated in the lower paid groups (which still persists today), but did not allow this to affect their work.

Despite the high standards that are maintained by the Fire Service, the equipment wasn't always of the highest quality, but it was

the best available. In the 1950s the firemen of the RAF Fire Service were issued with one pair of gumboots; one pair of brown denim overalls; a leather jerkin of WW1 and 2 vintage; a steel helmet that had been modified with an asbestos visor and into which was fitted a glass window (which became obscured in the first few minutes in smoke); and a pair of gloves. In the 1980s, the personal gear has improved considerably.

AC Tony Eaton joined the RAF in October 1955 for four years, went through the usual eight-week conversion of civvy to serviceman via the square, and was then posted to the RAF School of Fire Fighting at RAF Sutton-on-Hull for a nine-week course which he

Fitting, or removing, the Martin Baker ejection seat from a Hawker Hunter F6.
(Bruce Robertson.)

A trainee fire fighter in full kit at the School of Fire Fighting at RAF Manston in 1977. The kit is being continually improved. (MOD.)

To see all three runways the 'crash line' was sited in a metal hut on the other side of the airfield from the Air Traffic Control (ATC), and conditions were primitive: Elsans and a spade in place of running water toilets, and no drinking water, which had to be brought in. An old barrack-room type stove completed the décor. The vehicles were a Mk 5A foam tender with a foam output of 1900 gals/minute (8640 litres/minute), a Land-Rover, a CO_2 gas truck, a Bedford water bowser and a Coventry Climax trailer pump. At that time the A1 ran across the approach path to runway 04-22, which was to cause some problems when flying started.

The increased flying had its effect mainly in small fires caused by wet starts when accumulated fuel was ignited, or in aircraft swinging off the runway after tyre punctures. But there was an incident in 1957 — LAC Eaton's first prang. He writes, 'The first prang I attended was a Valetta that was doing a one-engined overshoot and when the pilot applied power to the good engine, it pulled him lower and it crashed about five miles from the station in a cornfield. This happened in August and the road skirting the cornfield was really busy with holiday traffic. The aircraft flew across the road in between the

One service institution that is necessary. Fire fighters at RAF Leeming on duty in 1957. The clothing they wear was part of the kit then issued but since has been considerably redesigned for the job. (A. E. Eaton).

enjoyed with the enthusiasm of one who was doing what he wanted. AC Eaton says his career in the RAF Fire Service, and subsequently the Air Ministry Fire Service, is typical of 99% of any of them. Maybe it is, but quite a number of fire service personnel can actually go through their service without being involved in an aircraft fire or crash.

After the course, the subjects of which were to be more important than at most schools, as will be understood later, AC Eaton was posted as an Aerodrome Fireman/Driver to RAF Leeming in the North Riding. Leeming was a large airfield which was being constructionally prepared to operate as 228 Operational Conversion Unit (OCU) with Gloster Javelin night fighters and, later, V bombers, by new taxiways, dispersal areas, runway extensions — Leeming had three runways — and a large flight line area.

Typical spectacular training scene as trainee fire fighters tackle a simulated aircraft type incident at the School of Fire Fighting at RAF Sutton-on-Hill. (Bruce Robertson).

traffic, its props cutting into the tarmac of the road.

'The fuel tanks were ruptured as it slid along on its belly, but the pilot, a Sergeant, and his pupil climbed out without a scratch. We received the call by — wait for it — a wartime field telephone. We received the garbled message over this contraption and after an initial scout in the wrong direction, we finally made it to the map reference. I must confess to a feeling of schoolboyish excitement at speeding down the road swinging on the bell and seeing all the traffic separate for us. We eventually arrived to a scene of dozens of cars and people milling around. I am pleased to say there was no fire, but we covered the spilt fuel with foam. The aircrew were treated for shock and sent back to Leeming.'

In the spring of 1958 occurred another

incident, as these events are called, in which the training of all ranks in the use of fire extinguishers bore fruit, and there was great co-operation between the fire services, both RAF and civilian, and good organisation. Let SAC Eaton relate it in his own words: 'I was on crash duty, this time on the Land-Rover light rescue. At about 0930 hours I heard a very loud explosion come from No. 2 hangar, on looking we could see the glow of the very obvious fire in the hangar. We ran to our vehicles and went straight across the runway after getting clearance. My vehicle was first on the scene, being the fastest. I ran into the hangar with a 10lb CO^2 extinguisher and was confronted with three blazing aircraft. A Javelin, a Meteor 7 and a Vampire were in varying degrees of fire and setting fire to the roof of the hangar. The foam tender was a minute or so behind our vehicle; it went straight into the hangar and proceeded to fight the fire of the Meteor.

'The hangar staff by this time were beginning to get the first-aid appliances to work and starting to open the hangar doors, to try and evacuate the aircraft that were not affected. I must pay tribute to the hangar staff who were really terrific, they got stuck in with hoses and equipment that we gave them, and did as they were told. Also aircrew came to help and they were just as good and helpful. By now the hangar was well ablaze and the Meteor was almost gutted. The time lapse was about six minutes, this shows how bad the situation was.

'The local authority Fire Brigade arrived some 15 minutes later, and they began to fight the fire on the top of the roof, using extended ladders. After about an hour and a half, the fire was extinguished and the salvage clearing started. By the early afternoon the hangar was clear and the floor washed down, we then managed to get something to eat. The cost was £11,000 for the hangar roof, and the price of a Meteor 7, a badly damaged Javelin Mk 5 and a badly blistered Vampire.'

After the Falklands campaign RAF Stanley was considerably enlarged with a new runway capable of accepting the largest aircraft, including Tristar tankers. For these aircraft, specially developed Gloster Saro Mk.11 Javelin foam tenders were based on Ascension Island – the half-way mark – and at Stanley in 1985. (Q. and C. Eaton).

So great was Tony Eaton's interest in his fireman career that on completion of his RAF engagement he joined the Air Ministry Fire Service at RAF Leeming. Acutely aware of the image that was then prevalent, he says, 'As a civvy, we are treated with much greater respect. If I may add that the fire service has always had to take its share of mickey-taking, which is fair enough, as they do their share of cockups, but, if people would remember that the fireman has to remember all of his training and get it right in a couple of minutes. There is no time to study the technical manuals on the way. So it's not surprising that there are mistakes made. It is this that is in the fireman's mind when he is on the way to an incident. So if criticism and a bit of mickey-taking are handed out, it should be tempered with that thought. I hope you don't mind me saying this, even though it has nothing to do with the story.' It has.

Part of the cold war philosophy was to build the most fearsome weapons known to man and, of course, test them. For the British that place was Christmas Island, a tiny island in the Pacific. To this place came the Comets, Hastings, Valiants and Shackletons, staging through the American-based staging posts from the UK. Atomic bomb tests had previously been carried out over Maralinga, S. Australia, the first drop being made by a 49 Squadron Valiant on 11 October 1956.

On Monday 28 April 1958, the then ultimate destructive device, the H bomb, was tested and many RAF tradesman were indirectly involved, because their duties required them to be there. So they were issued with special clothing and directed as to the programme to be maintained when the bomb was dropped. The carrier aircraft was a Valiant and, when it finally took off on a sunny day, all the troops were kept in touch through Tannoy speakers with its progress. An interesting but vital point was that all airmen were cleared from the take-off area, in case the Valiant crashed on take-off — the danger was not from an explosion but a leakage of radioactivity. Senior Tech Hughes says there was much black comedy among the

men and they looked very vulnerable. Before the aircraft took off, the men had to dress in long trousers, shirts, long socks, shoes, white anti-flash suits, hoods and gloves.

The tension really heightened when the announcer called that the weapon had been dropped from the aircraft and the count-down came through to explosion point. The men sat with their backs to the expected explosion and after a count-down to 15 seconds, the count began to go up. At plus five seconds the sky lit up. The men were required to close their eyes and cover them with their hands. There were no anti-flash goggles or face guards. The heat from the blast was very noticeable and after plus 15 seconds they were given permission to view the bomb point (through sunglasses). It was the now familiar mushroom of boiling clouds and smoke that attracted so dramatically, but they were unprepared for the blast that followed which came before the sound of the explosion and was felt distinctly.

The sight and sound must have left an indelible mark in the minds of the men who saw the results of what highly intelligent and brilliant men can do in the cause of destruction. Many must have thought deeply about it later.

Each hydrogen bomb test was given the overall codeword 'Grapple' suffixed by a letter as shown below:

15 May 1957	Grapple W
8 November 1957	Grapple X
28 April 1958	Grapple Y
September 1958	Grapple Z

But before the testing could be carried out, the base at Christmas Island had to be established, for the original USAAF airfield put down during the war had been deserted for some years and required refurbishing. The airfield became well populated with all three services plus civilians from the Atomic Energy Authority, all living in tented accommodation; four-man tents for Officers and SNCOs and marquees for Corporals and below.

The island had none of the romantic tropical aura, but scrub and palm trees eased the eyes. There was plenty of concrete with extra acres being added by courtesy of a hard-working section of the REs. Water came from a borehole and had to be treated for drinking; lighting was primitive and uncertain and was supplied by a generator maintained by 'a Navy character straight from the old Players packet'. The Mess was well lighted, however, 'so profits soared according to voltage'. A regular RAF detachment was in residence with a transport group of Dakotas and Hastings and 22 Squadron Whirlwinds. Build up of aircraft and personnel increased as the test date approached and from a comparatively leisurely beginning Senior Tech Hughes and Company of 240 Squadron were soon busy readying their Shackletons for the varied operations required.

Jim Hughes' journey by squadron Shackleton to Christmas Island had been rather eventful. He had been detailed to take a replacement engine to another aircraft U/S at Travis Field, California. The engine was stowed in the bomb bay by means of a special engine stand and bomb doors and after a slight snag in which the bomb doors had been fitted in reverse, causing the engine to project about four feet (and the NCO in charge of the job rumoured to have committed hara kiri), the aircraft took off.

Bad weather forced them down at St. Mawgan, but the next stop was Lagos,

Shackleton R-R Griffon engine change at Barksdale Field, USA, when aircraft was en route to Christmas Island for bomb test work. April 1958. (J. Hughes.)

Portugal, where they were well treated by our oldest allies. Next stop was the Azores and then a long trip of over 13 hours to Bermuda. From there, Charleston in South Carolina was their first stop on American territory. Here they were given a typical welcome and entertained. The best bit of fun came on their next leg, to Biggs Field in Texas, when No.2 engine went U/S, the propeller was feathered

A Shackleton Mk.2, WR 965, of the type used by No. 240 Squadron in which S/Tech Hughes flew to Christmas Island. (MOD.)

and they diverted to Barksdale, a Strategic Air Command base with B-47s. The elderly Shackleton looked rather antique in their company. The No. 2 engine was diagnosed as having a broken inclined drive shaft — and the spare engine they were carrying was used. As Jim remarked, 'which rather defeated the object of our mission'. They reached Christmas Island after 5 days and 69 flying hours.

It is probably true to say that, at its peak, the V bomber force was superior to any air force in the world, but its continuing efficiency was halted by economic reasons (as usual) and the advent of the Polaris submarine. After that vessel came into service, the Victor and Vulcan were placed under the operational jurisdiction of NATO for use as a long range tactical strike/recce aircraft with conventional bombs, but retaining nuclear capability. In the latter role there were several squadrons, notably those

A form of security that was considered satisfactory for the V-bombers in the late 1950s and 1960s but hardly sufficient today. The aircraft is a Valiant. (MOD.)

based at RAF Scampton, which stayed in that role until they were either re-equipped with the new Tornado or were disbanded. In fact, the last of the V squadrons were phased out in the late 1970s and the aircraft, except the Vulcan, converted to tankers.

The rehearsed aim of 'standby readiness' was to have two or four bombers at the take-off end of the runway with crews strapped in, all systems operating, but no engines running. On receipt of the alarm signal 50 Squadron at RAF Waddington would have all four of their Vulcans airborne in 90 seconds. The Vulcan B1As of Chief Tech Turner's squadron were electrically started and the secret of fast start up was 'a Simm starter trolley full of batteries, which was plugged into the aircraft starter circuit! The aim of the ground crew was when the captain's legs were just vanishing up the ladder, all buttons were pressed and all four engines were running when he got to his seat'. The 90-second start was eventually deemed too dangerous.

The V bombers were equipped with electronic countermeasures against enemy rockets, air-to-air missiles and fighter interception. Results: more specialist knowledge required. The aircrew knew how to operate the gear, even to do minor repairs in the air — very minor — but, if the equipment failed, it was up to the tradesmen on the ground to fix — as usual.

Towards the end of their operational lives the Valiants, first of the V bombers, were converted for use as air-to-air tankers. In August 1964 during routine servicing it was discovered that the main spar had fatigue cracks and all aircraft were grounded. As they were nearing the end of their useful lives and the cost of repairing the spars was very high, it was finally decided to withdraw them all from service in February 1965. During their service, they had proved to be versatile aircraft. Because of their inbuilt efficiency, the V bombers were easily adapted to 'cockpit readiness' tactics during a particular period of unease and the standby aircraft were parked, ready to scramble by the runway. A Blue Alert gave 30 minutes' readiness, a 'cockpit readiness' was four minutes.

A Vulcan B2 of No. 617 Squadron with Blue Steel missile in position and tests and checks being photographed. The tyres are covered against possible contamination from missile fuel. About 1959/60. (Bruce Robertson collection.)

The Blue Steel stand-off bomb, designed for the Vulcan and Victor, was meant to be a back-up for the American Skybolt, but as the latter was scrapped by the USAF in 1963, Blue Steel became an interim weapon with a comparatively short life. The bomb was powered by a Stenton two-chamber rocket motor, using liquid propellant fuel and was navigated by an inertial guidance system. Its introduction into the RAF brought the need for special fitters and Electronic (Air) Technicians to service the rocket motor and the inertial guidance system. The use of high test peroxide fuel meant that care was needed when refuelling, and protection was required for the ground crews. So the Fire Service became quite technical also. When a Blue Steel was being refuelled or practice loaded into a V bomber, the fire and crash crew were required to don special rubberoid suits and

Blue Steel air to ground radio controlled missile designed for use with V bombers, undergoing checks in storage. Photo shows well the Stentor rocket motor. (Bruce Robertson).

headgear and stand by with a 1000 gall (4546 L) water tender for spraying the bomb if it became too hot. It was never necessary.

Senior Tech Harry Turner started his course for Aircraft Servicing Chief on the Vulcan with six weeks' engine training in November 1960 at RAF Weeton, followed by basic electrical training at RAF Melksham, where the SWO's pride and joy, a large pond stuffed with goldfish, was converted by two non-ASC trainees from a large one with many small fish, to a large one with one large satisfied fish — a pike which they had caught and introduced into the pond. The SWO was not amused. After Melksham, Harry spent three months at Woodford, home of the Vulcan, but was billeted out in Wilmslow, formerly a training school for RAF and WAAF, before being posted to 230 OCU at RAF Finningley for a period.

A detachment to RAF Coningsby provided an amusing highlight in 1962. The resident Vulcan squadron, just forming, was commanded by a super efficient CO who was determined his squadron would be the best and he 'did everything by the book'. One of the Vulcans of Turner's detachment was 'a pig to start . . . we used the Rover AAPP to feed air to No.3 or 4, started one, opened up to 60% and cross-fed air to start the rest, as the Rover didn't have the guts to cross-feed.

'Anyway, this day it wouldn't go. Two tries each at 3 and 4 and the skipper told me the crew were getting out until I'd fixed it. So they did and, as this was going on we noticed smoke coming out of the intake, common enough, hot air and oil, but we took no chances and called for 'Crash one' the Land-Rover, to stand by while we investigated. That's what we got at base, but this was

With the acceptance into the RAF of the new V class bombers, much ground support equipment was redesigned for use with them. Among them was special aircraft towing tractors with their drivers specifically trained. This photograph of a group of new production Vulcan Mk. I's in 1957, two of which display the badge of No. 230 OCU on the fin, are being marshalled for the day's flying. The Vulcan, in its two main Mark 1 and 2 forms, stayed in service until 1984 and was the only V bomber 'blooded' by being used operationally in the Falklands campaign. (MoD)

The transition of World War 2 piston-engined bombers were made by the English Electric Canberra, a three-seater aircraft which proved to be most efficient and long-lived, entering service in 1951 and serving for over 10 years when the Vee bombers finally superseded them. A total of well over 600 of all marks were built for the RAF. The Canberra was used operationally in the Suez crisis in October 1956, being based on Malta as the photograph shows. (MoD).

Coningsby and the Wing Commander had issued his orders.

'We got Crash one. We also got two Mk. 5 tenders, the big Mk. 7 came across the grass at 70 mph, we got the SMO (Senior Medical Officer) driving his ambulance, the Senior Mechanical Transport Officer (SMTO) in the Tugmaster, his junior (JMTO) in the Coles Crane, the Station Commander, the Wingco (of course), the SWO and, five minutes later, the Tattershall Fire Brigade. They all stood around like vultures while we dropped the engine doors, investigated, closed the doors, put the crew in and the so-and-so started first time!'

As a measure of the importance of the V bomber force it was given top priority in spares demands and so on, top rating being Victor/Vulcan on Ground (VOG). On one night occasion at RAF Finningley, ASC Turner wanted a 1/16 inch split pin, of which there were none in store, so Turner signalled off a VOG to obtain one. This incident caused a posting from the stores! And, split pins being the subject of this paragraph, Turner tells the tale of a friend of his who ran the Motor Club at Waddington and was pestered by an aircrew member: "Have you got a split pin, Chief?" Harry dived into his toolbag and produced a $\frac{1}{2}$ inch diameter by 9 inch long split pin. "No, Chief, smaller than that". So, out of the bag came a $\frac{1}{32}$ inch by $\frac{1}{2}$ inch long pin, and he had no trouble after that!'

The squadron's mascot was a snow-white St. Bernard with whom they had fun. 'Beautiful animal, overweight when it was acquired at $10\frac{1}{2}$ stone (67kg). But as thick as two short planks and it used to dribble. Didn't need its barrel, presented by Hennessey the brandy people, but should have had a drip tray!'

To illustrate how efficient the V force became, the account of a detachment to Akrotiri by eight Vulcans of 50 Squadron will suffice. ASC Turner and all the required ground crews had been airlifted by Argosy to Akrotiri before the Vulcans arrived — at night. The station was also geared to play its part and the eight Vulcans were refuelled, re-armed, inspected and airborne within 90 minutes from first touchdown to last wheels off. During the turnround, an airman armed with binoculars and in a vehicle fitted with a powerful searchlight had driven slowly down the line inspecting the air intakes through the glasses.

On a lighter note, the personnel of 50 Squadron became film stars for a few seconds, when episodes of the James Bond film *Thunderball* were filmed at Waddington, lasting a couple of days and with six or seven takes for a 30-second sequence. ASC Harry Turner, one of the RAF's stars, made it on the wide screen but not for TV. However, as he wrote, 'afterwards we had a booze up on the film company and today, I still don't like vodka martini, shaken or stirred!'

Today, with the aid of the microchip, a rapid increase in knowledge in all aeronautical fields as a result of adequate research and development programmes, plus a final realisation that the sharing of design effort and costs is essential, a whole new generation of aircraft and associated equipment is being supplied to NATO forces and back-up units; the Jaguar, Harrier and Tornado are examples. The microchip has enabled bombs and rockets to be delivered more accurately and the new materials have enabled these devices to be made smaller with an increase in destructive power, so enabling smaller aircraft to be built and virtually making the large bomber aircraft obsolete. Similar changes have taken place in the related fields of navigation, communication, armament, engine design and so on.

One result of continuing aircraft development has been a major change in

HS Harrier of No. 20 Squadron being serviced in a hide in RAF Germany. Note the 30mm gun pod, one of two and the somewhat inconvenient ladder used for cockpit access.

(Bruce Robertson collection.)

hangar design, forced upon the designers by the very real threat of attacks on airfields putting out of action multi-million pound aircraft. Ideally, the dispersal potential of the Harrier sets the standard, but not all aircraft have the unique VTOL capabilities of that aeroplane and all expensive aircraft have to be protected. Their complexity requires that they be near a source of technical supply: air, oxygen, hydraulics, electrical power, black box spares and so on.

In response to this requirement, the hardened aircraft shelter, first introduced into NATO use and sited in dispersed patterns to minimise effects of low level attack, have developed successfully enough to become the standard hangar on selected back-up airfields for NATO units in the UK. These steel and concrete hangars have electrically controlled doors and all necessary services piped into them from an independent source to make the HAS completely self-contained. Working inside one exposes the ground crew to potential but definite danger as the HAS will naturally be a prime target in the event of a hot war.

Since 1945 world-wide unrest has led to confrontations and open conflict throughout the world — in Korea, Vietnam, Israel and the Arab countries, Hungary, South America, Africa and so on. Britain was soon involved in crises which occasionally stretched her resources. To explain all these events would require a bigger book than this, but many were purely political, some ideological, others nationally inspired. Whatever the cause the RAF was called in to give its support to Britain's particular problems on many occasions.

Chapter 4
. . . And Hot

This account of the RAF's participation in overseas events is a story more of withdrawal than rebuild. Despite this, the RAF has been involved in many crises, emergencies and campaigns in which its manpower has gained much valuable experience.

Most of the RAF's actions have taken place in the fifties. The Malayan campaign, the longest for over 100 years, dragged on from 1948 to 1960 and was one of recce, supply, strike and bombing against a very small force virtually invisible in its own territory. In 1953 a more serious outbreak of the fighting in the Aden Protectorates took place, and engaged the attentions of most units in that theatre. This operation ceased in 1954 only to flare up again in 1955 and to continue spasmodically until the withdrawal of forces from Aden in 1967. The Kuwait crisis occurred during 1961. Except for the Sunderlands and Austers, the RAF played only an indirect part in Korea by helping the Royal Australian Air Force (RAAF) and United States Air Force (USAF), and using Transport Command to bring in men and materials. The crisis lasted from 1950 until 1953, but the efforts of the Commonwealth pilots did help to explode the myth of the Russian MiG 15. In Kenya, a similar but shorter campaign to that of Malaya kept the British forces in action against the Mau Mau from 1952 until its conclusion in 1955. In 1956 another major crisis occurred when Egypt was invaded by the forces of Britain and France and set the pattern of short wars — it raged for seven days in November but was hardly a contested event against a country which had not fought independently for a hundred years. The pattern was followed by the Falklands Emergency of 1982, but with a new strategy, that of very long range supply and attack by the RAF, made possible only by the evolution of air-to-air refuelling, and with close co-operation with the Royal Navy Fleet Air Arm. Of minor crises there were plenty: Zimbabwe, Cyprus, Belize, Northern Ireland, Bangladesh, Palestine, Indonesia were some events that kept the RAF on its toes and a chance for ground crews to experience the turbulent state of the world.

The Malaya conflict evolved from the determination by the early Malayan Communist Party (MCP) of 1929 to overthrow the ruling Administration. Although in its early days it did not make much progress, the advent of the Japanese conflict in the mid-1930s led to a truce between the Chinese Communist Party and the Kuomintang Party in order to fight the Japanese. This gave the MCP the opportunity it needed and it began to form cells within Malaya, which increased in size and efficiency to become an organised underground party and an agent of the British when they declared war on the Japanese. After the initial British defeat the strength of the MCP was such that it was the only force organised to promote resistance against the occupying Japanese and it was supplied with arms and ammunition by the British. Despite clashes with rival organisations, whom it defeated, when peace was finally declared the MCP began to return to its original aims: first to co-operate with and then to infiltrate authority while carrying out its revolutionary policy.

In 1948, with Russian Communist backing, the MCP came out into the open with armed insurrection, which took the form of sabotage, murder and terrorism and formed a field unit, the Malayan Races Liberation Army (MRLA). The new MRLA was highly efficient in its destructive role, and with first-hand knowledge of the country it terrorised and lived off the local population, using arms it had saved from the Japanese occupation and a limited number of supplied weapons. At its peak in 1957 it had about 8000 members. The long campaign developed into one of attrition until the final phase in 1960 when, reduced to about 500 active MRLA, it was finally declared on 31 July 1960 as ended.

In the 12 years during which this undeclared war simmered, a technically inferior jungle force, armed with little more than small arms and mortars, utilised its knowledge of the country and ruthless terrorism on the local population to keep a highly trained and sophisticated modern force in a state of emergency and on a war footing. It was the jungle that was the greatest factor in the conflict. Saturation with bombs and cannon on the suspected Communist Terrorist (CT) encampments was much like cracking a nut with a sledgehammer, but it was absolutely necessary in that situation.

The RAF operated up-country in Malaya from Kuala Lumpur (KL) in close support of the army, with its rear bases at Changi, Seletar and Tengah on Singapore Island. The Advanced Air HQ was at KL, the rear Air HQ at Changi.

To give an idea of the involvement of the RAF throughout the long emergency and the first-class experience gained, a total of 28 squadrons operating 26 different types of aircraft, from Austers to Valiants, served during the emergency. Of these, 16 squadrons operated detachments from the UK, mainly bomber units, with Lincoln (7), Canberra B6 (4), Canberra PR7 (5) and Valiant (2). The variety of aircraft emphasises the ground equipment and spares problems that had to be solved, not only in the operational theatres but in the staging posts *en route*. The aircraft represent a good cross-section of the RAF's types during this period.

Such a long drawn out conflict ensured that a great proportion of serving airmen, and a number of airwomen, were posted to the Malayan theatre and associated bases such as staging posts, some of the airmen doing two tours. The early postings did the long sea journey by troopship and in Malaya worked on WW2 aircraft; those who arrived near the end of the campaign travelled by air and worked on post-war and jet aircraft.

In the early days one of the aircraft used was the Mosquito PR34, developed for photo reconnaissance and used by 81 Squadron, on which served LAC Harry Turner. Apparently, the squadron had great licence in 'bulling' the aircraft well beyond the standard finish. 'We took delight in "prettying up' . . . with official blind eyes, of course. Squadron crests, black cleat lines, coloured spinners, a playing card — 81 had an unofficial badge of the ace of spades nicked, I believe from a German unit. We painted the playing card roundel size, alongside the fuselage roundel! We didn't have our "own" machines, just favourites'. The aircraft must have looked like a cross between Richthofen's Circus and an American fighter.

The Mosquito was excellent at its job but the steamy humid atmosphere of Malaya was against the 'wood and glue' construction: the reason why was soon revealed and led to it being withdrawn. It was one of Turner's all-time great favourites but 'We sometimes lost the odd one — the undercarriages couldn't take a sideways load and Seletar wasn't the easiest of airfields. Not an easily repairable structure, but we saved them for Nov 5 bonfire. Put one Cat 5 one day as exceeding its fatigue life and it had about six weeks . . . in the dump before the Salvage boys came along and saw it. Then, out of the mainplane marched a colony of white ants — or some such beasts. We were very wary of the rest of the squadron (aircraft) from then . . . '.

During this period, the operations against the terrorists required a disproportionately large number of men, both Army and RAF, and an equally heavy use of bombs in all their different types, even the use of defoliant chemicals, leaflet dropping, loud hailers mounted in Dakotas and psychological warfare tactics. It does seem that the campaign became an opportunity for testing various methods of modern warfare — all except defence against a modern western-style enemy.

For the airmen the advantage of service in Malaya was the experience of real operations, albeit against an almost unseen enemy of passionate belief in their political ideology, while doing their work from modern comfortable stations well behind the operational area. There was good access to the delights of Singapore Island, which included a new NAAFI club built opposite the Raffles Hotel and a popular old-fashioned Union Jack Club. Most married airmen were housed in good quality MQs or in decent rented houses. During the operations, some political and social rapport with the peoples of Singapore and Malaya was made which endured after the conflict, although, as Senior Tech Honeybone said, 'as our workmates . . . were mainly Indians, Malays, Chinese and sundry Eurasians . . . there was always the danger of CT infiltration so we made friends carefully!.'

On the deficit side, the campaign was a very expensive business and was probably maintained to avoid losing face with the East. To the long service airman there was the probability of another tour to an area where tropical diseases could still be caught, though these were efficiently contained by enforcing strict hygiene and medical standards. For those airmen working up-country on the isolated airstrips there was the possibility of moments of extreme danger from dedicated killers.

But to the West the conflict that was going on in this jungle country became almost a forgotten one, probably because of the lack of fierce Korean-type actions and, fortunately, the very low casualties. The campaign was one of steady attrition year in, year out; experimenting with ways to end it; the

Casualties from overseas flown in by Comet being transferred to ambulances at RAF St. Mawgan in November 1958. (RAF Official.)

71

evaluation of different types of aircraft; steadily rising costs; strikes; supply dropping; and casualty evacuation that became almost routine. The helicopters' role in this operation was one reason why fatal casualties were so low. Taking 12 years to conclude, Operation Firedog was not one of the great successes.

As a general rule the majority of RAF airmen see very little of the effects of their efforts in terms of physical damage; most are well back from the theatre of operations. Those who are closer to the scene of action, for example at forward airstrips, are normally well protected by army units. Since WW2 the major campaigns in which the RAF has been involved have been with peoples who have lacked expertise in modern warfare, and who have not had the equipment anyway — the Malayan Communists, the Kikuyu tribes of Kenya, the irregulars of Oman and Aden Protectorates. Even the short sharp action at Suez against Egypt was against a people with little experience of modern warfare. The smaller actions were in the same mould. Consequently there may have been a certain amount of nonchalance among the ground trades.

But if there was no danger in Malaya from a force attacking according to the rules of war, there certainly was by the stealthy hand of guerillas, terrorists and the equivalent of irregular commandos. Tight station security was enforced, aircraft were guarded, quite

Loading an HS Argosy at Labuan, Sabah, with a one ton supply container for dropping to forward troops. About 1964.

(Bruce Robertson collection.)

often by local levies, and armed escorts were provided for convoys carrying families in a suspect area. At times of possible infiltrations by the enemy, married quarters and hirings were guarded. Senior Tech Honeybone: 'War conditions were always close . . . one leave centre at Penang was open to other ranks but was not too popular as it meant travelling by train with the family through communist bandit territory and armed with a sten gun'.

At Changi a Jungle Survival School was instituted to teach the art of self-sufficiency in the Malayan jungle and to it came all air and ground personnel whose job necessitated flying over, and operating within, that forbidding flora. The school's teachings in understanding the psychological fear of being alone in the forest and bush was no doubt instrumental in saving a number of lives. The course was of two weeks' duration and successful enough for the Americans to attend; it instilled such awareness of the possible dangers that few who had attended the course ever mislaid their survival packs. These packs were of lightweight jungle green material, roughly 15 in (38cm) by 8 in (20cm), and contained a water bottle, emergency rations, small first aid kit, a piece of green nylon parachute material, poncho, spare socks and shirt, a packet of three contraceptives and a small elastic band. Contraceptives in the jungle? And no spare elastic band? They were worn over the penis and secured by the band to prevent the entry of small leeches and other parasites. Chief Tech Milner: 'thought I was being had until the CO did his Jungle Survival course and got a leech on his scrotum',

Nearly all operational sorties were of short duration so ground crews had little spare time. The strike squadrons were geared to operate at short notice to catch the CTs before they moved far, which meant the ground crews had to be on the alert, aircraft ready to move with starter trolleys plugged in. Meals and other vital functions would be taken on an overlap, or shift, system and each day would be a full one from dawn to dusk.

Out in the bush, it was found that the most effective way to deal with the terrorists was by the costly method of bombing, using heavy and medium size bombs. Also, to this end, two delightful weapons were employed, 350 lb (158 kg) clusters of 19 lb (9kg) fragmentation bombs and the defoliating chemicals. The 1970 HMSO publication *The Malayan Emergency 1948-1960,* is an excellent definitive history containing masses of detailed statistics of operations, supplies and transportation activities of the RAF, behind which can be glimpsed, though it is not detailed, some idea of the work of the ground crews. It is from that history that the following cost of bombs (at 1951 prices) are taken:

1000 lb (454 kg)	£125
500 lb (227 kg)	£56
20 lb (18 kg)	£4.10s
60 lb (27 kg) rockets	£18.10s

In the supply drops, where many hundreds of parachutes were used on a one-use basis, cost was also a major factor. The original R type supply parachute which could carry 450lb (204 kg) cost £32; the 180 lb (82 kg) Irvin cost £15. So a utility type was introduced which cost £21 - £26. Despite the tremendous amount of ammunition used against the terrorists, which would not have disgraced a small European war, this was still one of the first campaigns fought with some regard to cost-effectiveness.

At Tengah there were facilities for day and night major servicing and maintenance which were used to the full. The longer range aircraft ensured that most ground crew operated from rear airfields which gave the airmen reasonably good living conditions. For the short range Pioneers, Austers and the helicopters, the erks often lived in more

During the Malayan campaign a Hunter FGA9 of 20 Squadron undergoes a rapid turnround at RAF Tengah. The 30mm gun pack is being fitted. (Bruce Robertson)

Arms to be carried at all times! An RAF Regiment camp at RAF Sepulot, Malaya, showing issue tents and local built hut. (RAF Official.)

primitive conditions, right up and into enemy territory, to be able to service and supply their charges. The ground crew at Tengah and other stations on Singapore Island had the advantage of permanent accommodation with all services laid on and the pleasures of occasional trips to Singapore City where they could relax (and get occasionally fleeced) in the most pleasant way.

Up-country, erks at Kuala Lumpur were confined to the station during the more hectic years of the campaign, because of possible infiltration by the guerillas into the station area. They were also at full stretch all day and Kuala Lumpur was crowded with aircraft; so

it was fortunate that the terrorists did not operate commando infiltrators as the serried ranks of aircraft belonging to the four squadrons presented a mouth-watering target. Life at Kuala Lumpur, once the men were acclimatised to the conditions, was quite good in the stone and brick barrack blocks. Dress was informal, mainly shorts and 'flip flops'. The squadrons flew from dawn to dusk and kept one Sycamore on emergency standby together with a duty pilot who assisted where needed. Work was on a two-shift system and many junior tradesmen had the opportunity to fly on some missions as a useful man for any technical troubles and for overnight stops and to act as stewards on troop-lifting duties. Other duties of the squadrons included casualty evacuation, flying in doctors, medical supplies, food, equipment, collecting bods, VIPs, crew training and routine visits to the jungle forts.

The Sycamore was one of the earliest helicopters and this was reflected in its type of construction. The main rotors were hand-made by elderly aircraft carpenters who had been brought out of retirement by Bristol. As a result, each blade had a slightly different performance and all three blades required 'tuning' or tracking to get optimum performance. Each blade was crayoned with a different colour and the rotor was turned at the scheduled speed — this was done by a pilot in case of ground interference or lift-off — and a tracking flag was then gently nudged into the disc. A good track showed the colours superimposed on each other, and track was adjusted by varying the incidence of the required blade at the main rotor head. The aircraft also required a lot of mechanical maintenance, continual greasing of the transmission shafts and bearings and the small undercarriage wheels particularly. When being towed, it was vital to grease the wheels every few hundred yards! While doing this on one occasion Chief Tech Milner had a large audience of locals 'who weren't sure if we were worshipping or feeding this strange thing'.

First job every day was to test the duty chopper for acceptable vertical lift: 'no point landing in a jungle clearing if you can't vertical out. If the vertical wasn't up to scratch we'd try and tune the rotor first by tracking and then by adjusting the fixed trim tabs on the trailing edge of each main blade. The tabs would be moved usually in 20 thou steps gauged by a DTI specially mounted and issued as part of the aircraft kit.'

The stage of development of these aircraft was such that its squadron lost aircraft from forced landings from engine failures and two fatal accidents caused by rotor blade failures, which were attributed to the glued joints of the blades being unable to withstand the climate and stresses of jungle operation.

Those erks operating the Dragonflies of 194 Squadron had the added experience of occasionally going into the jungle clearings to assist the choppers in lifting out army personnel. To help in this, army sappers may have had to clear a space among the trees with explosives. The Whirlwinds of 155 Squadron had short-life rotor blades and hubs, which required the servicing and replacing of any that seemed suspect and this could be a sweaty business in an airless clearing. The main task of handling Sycamores in even smaller clearings might befall the ground crews of 194 Squadron.

The faithful Dakota, veteran of many a campaign involving uplift of men or materials, had been converted to carry heavy loads of voice broadcasting gear, but it too had a spares problem — that of finding sufficient replacement Pratt & Whitney R1830 engines, for after 13 years of heavy use that reliable engine had been phased out of production. And there was the added disadvantage that the same engine type was installed in the Sunderlands of 205 Squadron, who were doing a great job in bomber, air-sea rescue, recce, anti-piracy patrol and transport roles. The venerable Sunderlands were phased out during the campaign and ignominiously sold for scrap — no doubt without the valuable Pratt & Whitney engines. When on air-sea rescue work they could be airborne in one hour by day, two by night; a very good time for it included crews to dinghy and on to aircraft, starting up, casting off and taxying to the take-off point. The flying-boat ground crew would be waiting aboard, engines primed, and an erk in the retracted front turret space was ready with the cast-off gear. The ground crew would return in the aircrew dinghy.

Number 656 AOP Squadron was continuously engaged against the CTs throughout the whole campaign with Austers Mks 5,6,9 and T7. Sorties increased to a total of 145,500 to the end of the crisis and the aircraft were used for liaison, visual reconnaissance, small tactical supply drops, leaflet drops, casevacs and target-marking strikes. Operating the Austers seems an obviously easier proposition than a Spitfire or Brigand, and so it is. But the role and ability of this small aircraft to operate into and out of small rough fields brings a different dimension to its ground crews, be they RAF or army. Servicing may not take up much time but sorties were short and frequent. The Austers is essentially a field aeroplane and in Malaya it fulfilled all that had been learned from its outstanding war record. The Austers of 656 Squadron did over 143,000 sorties (before handing over to the army), which is a lot of prop swinging! Incidentally, the turnover of Auster propellers as the result of climatic conditions (and bugs attacking the wood adhesive) was tremendous.

As was to be expected of this campaign, the men who endured the most hardships were the army troops and Malayan police. Six squadrons of the RAF Regiment (Malaya), 91 to 96 and HQ, with locally enlisted airmen, were in action and in a number of engagements they killed, wounded or captured nearly 80 CTs and destroyed nearly 300 camps. The Regiment earned 13 awards and 64 Mentions in Despatches. RAF casualties throughout the campaign were 74 killed and wounded.

Dave Bowers was posted in August 1961 to 81 Squadron at RAF Tengah, Singapore, the squadron having just converted from Meteor PR10s to Canberra PR7s. The squadron's main job was aerial survey of the area, but it was brought into the now diminishing Malaya emergency to do occasional recce sorties against the retreating terrorists near the border with Thailand. The squadron was responsible for its own servicing up to major inspections, with the result that most of the aircraft trades were engaged on that and rectification work. A 20-man team of all trades worked on the flight line, and was divided into two shifts, which changed over each week. First shift could start as early as 0400 for a post-Firedog sortie, and finished at midday, when it was relieved by the second shift, which worked until flying ceased and covered night flying when required.

During the Malaysian confrontation with Indonesia over British Borneo and Sarawak in 1963, the survey work was interrupted and the squadron engaged in recce work over Borneo, sending a two-aircraft detachment with ground crew support to Labuan. With the emergency influx of other aircraft, that small airfield was soon overcrowded; the men

AV-M N. M. Maynard, CB, CBE, DFC, AFC takes the salute as the Queen's Colours for FEAF are marched past in a final parade at RAF Singapore by No. 63 Squadron RAF Regiment. (MOD.)

at first were housed in tents, but the airfield construction units soon erected more substantial accommodation. The food was quite good considering the conditions and the use of open-air kitchens. A well-earned break was possible when an aircraft went back to Kai Tak, Hong Kong.

Aden was for a long time a vital centre for Britain's strategic defence, originally chosen to protect the Red Sea flank of the long sea route to India and beyond. A coaling station was laid down in Aden and, on the opening of the Suez Canal, this small untidy town assumed an even more vital importance. The Second World War and the rise of Arab nationalism, culminating in the takeover of the Suez Canal by Colonel Nasser, eroded Aden's position. Further power politics with Saudi Arabia, the departure of Britain from Iraq and the writing was on the wall. Internally, there had always been tribal conflict and the RAF had been there since 1918 with a Flight in a policing role. The country came under air control in 1928 and 8 Squadron was sent out in April of that year. The squadron stayed in the country, except for a few excursions in WW2, until the RAF left the area in 1967. A brief resumé of post-war actions will show the reader that the Aden Protectorates was the most disturbed of all the RAF's charges in the post-war period.

The Aden area stations comprised Khormaksar, Sheikh Othman, Socotra, Masirah, Salalah and Riyan, with Socotra closed down and Masirah, Salalah and Riyan on a care and maintenance basis in April 1946, each with a small contingent of 50 airmen, to service transport aircraft en route, for a six months' stay. The peaceful years that followed the end of WW2 in the area ended with the crisis of 1953 in Aden, caused in part by Saudi Arabia wishing to take over Buraimi Oasis for its important position on the crossroads of two major trade routes and, more importantly because there was the possibility of oil in the area. The oasis belonged officially to the Sultan of Muscat who was much concerned about it being occupied by a force of armed men led by a Saudi Arabian government official, Turki bin

Atuashan, whose action led the Sultan to seek aid. And so the RAF became involved.

First reinforcement aircraft into the theatre were Valettas and the Vampires of 6 Squadron from Habbaniya. There was a short official pause from October 1952 until March 1953, when ground reinforcements were increased and extra aircraft sent to Sharjah, along with two Flights of RAF armoured cars. A blockade was imposed on the Oasis by Vampires, and Meteor PR9s of 208 Squadron arrived from the Canal Zone to carry out photo recce. The dispute dragged on through 1954 until Turki was reported to be in Central Oman in January 1955. By this time many of the aircraft had returned to their bases. Those working at Sharjah had long spells of routine work interspersed with short bursts of 'on active service' type life, when working hours were as long as was necessary. As there was no outside entertainment it didn't really matter.

The blockade that commenced in March 1953 was not totally effective and the Lancasters of 683 Squadron used on recce were superseded by a Flight of six Ansons from Sharjah, which was now suffering overcrowding problems. Four Lancasters of 37 and 38 Squadrons were flown in from Malta to take over from the Meteors of 208 Squadron and with Habbaniya as their base. A final decision was made to capture the area where Turki's force was holed up and to assist the operations two Lincolns were based on Sharjah. In a successful army-RAF operation, the Trucial Oman Levies captured the villages and the Saudi fort and by October 1955 the Buraimi crisis was over.

In 1955, as a result of the changes of political emphasis, the Middle East was divided into two Groups:

1. AHQ Levant Cyprus: Cyprus, Jordan, Iraq, Libya, Canal Zone staging.
2. HQ British Forces Aden: Aden, East Africa, Pakistan, Persian Gulf, Southern Arabian Coast.

The RAF had hardly time to tidy up after the Buraimi Oasis operation before it was once again called in by the Sultan to help in another action caused by the illegal occupation of Central Oman at Nizwa by his rival, Imam Ghulib. Effective air operations in December 1955 caused the Imam to flee, but his brother carried on to become a costly thorn by his resistance, which lasted until 1957, Then a determined operation was begun, using all the resources of extra troops, fighter aircraft, bombers in the shape of Shackletons, howitzers and HMS *Bulwark,* but even then the operation dragged on until 1958 when a combined operation with SAS troops finally cleared the area and brought this long-lasting action to a close. The steady bombing imposed had had its effect.

The rough conditions of the airstrips used on the police actions and primitive ground handling generally associated from landing in a heavily loaded condition exacted its toll on the aircraft. The Vampire/Venom seemed not to be affected and were generally very successful on these operations. The high incidence of corrosive salt and sand affected the metal structure — on undercarriages and undersurfaces of main and tail planes, and in all crevices. MT was similarly affected. Treatment was assisted by plant washing machines installed at some cost, but they were affected by lack of fresh water and had to use purified sea water. Aircraft were returned to the UK in an incredible state (by RAF standards) of apparent neglect. On close internal inspection the effects of the corrosion, and the sand itself, would be found internally in the mainplanes and fuselages. Despite the latest anti-corrosive treatments this threat to aircraft aluminium alloys was always present and had to be rigidly controlled. No aircraft was ever lost as as result of corrosion.

The conditions on the Protectorate airfields were pretty rough, the main discomfort being the lack of natural shade. Day temperatures were usually a minimum of 80° (27°C) with constant high humidity, nil rainfall and dust storms from June to September. For example, Sharjah was 32°-130°F (0°-54°C); Aden 64°-105°F (18°-41°C). Masirah Island was 30 miles off the coast of Muscat and had the advantage of cooling winds off the sea. Sharjah had a natural surface runway which suffered from much erosion from the jets and during periods of heavy traffic, but surprisingly not from the Lancasters when they were brought in. A generous use of pierced steel planking (PSP) laid on suspect surfaces helped to prevent break-up.

The build-up of air transport traffic with larger and faster aircraft eventually reached the stage where sufficient were available for the new concept of mid-tour leave to be introduced, giving all ranks the opportunity to nip home: a much appreciated innovation, but one which was not to last long in the Middle East as Britain's services were gradually withdrawn.

For the operations carried out by 8 Squadron the Bristol Brigand was not quite suitable as a steady gun platform, or very manoeuvrable, and the decision was made to re-equip with Vampires. On the day of the offical handover of the new aircraft in April 1953 there was more than the normal movement on Khormaksar. LAC Roberts, who was serving in the Aden Protection Support Flight (APSF) said that 'Something Big' was to mark this memorable occasion: 'On the very morning that mattered our NCOs came and told us to organise makeshift flagstaffs out of the hangar brooms, to mount these on the window frames so as to point outwards like booms and slightly upward, and yellow dusters did duty as flags, mounted on string halyards on hastily rigged pulleys.

'None too soon either, for of a sudden we noticed the station band was assembling on the 8 Squadron apron, to our left. What was behind the band between the hangars we could not see until the fun started. The band came to attention, orders were shouted and the front line area resounded to the sound of the Slow March. The band wheeled to the right on setting off and came past our office and hangar, followed by a party of four mechanics carrying a full size coffin in which reposed the gleaming and polished undercarriage leg of a Brigand, raised slightly on a frame at the far end so that it could be clearly seen by all. Behind this spectacle was a party of a dozen or so officers, led by the Squadron Commander, very solemn and

Busy scene during a fast turnround of a No. 89 Squadron Venom at RAF Leconfield. One man refuelling, others replenishing with oxygen before aircrew have left the aircraft. In essence similar scenes are repeated at Aden. (RAF Official.)

melancholy of face. They were followed by the airfield tractor which was towing the last Brigand slowly along, festooned with black ribbons and accompanied by its bareheaded ground crew, all sporting black armbands, while bringing up the rear column was the remainder of the squadron personnel.

'As this cortege passed our site, the yellow dusters were duly lowered to half mast and caps doffed. Majestically, the whole procession wheeled to the left and crossed in front of us again, heading for a tour of the operational area and finishing up in the scrap compound where I understood a sort of drumhead service was held before the 8

Squadron pack, suddenly joyful, came back to the apron at the double and celebrated the advent of the Vampire age . . . .'

The Vampire and Meteor were two very good fighter aircraft which performed sterling service. The Vampire and its derivative, the Venom, had much action in Aden, Kenya and Trucial Oman and was used extensively in most overseas areas. The Meteor, while not as prolific overseas, was used in the photo recce role. Both aircraft had good serviceability records and this may have been as a result of the excellent courses given by the De Havilland works and RAF Cosford.

Loss of body fluid through excessive

sweating is a major cause of heat exhaustion as it dissipates the body salts, particularly dangerous in humid areas but just as bad in hot dry climates where the perspiration is not visible. A steady course of salt tablets usually keeps the complaint in check, the number of tablets taken varying with the conditions. In Egypt, two per day was considered sufficient; in Aden and similar places as many as 10-15 per day were necessary at times of intense stress, as when operating on a campaign in mid-summer. The effects of heat on the head and light through the eyes also contributed. The more distressing complaints were those caused by flies and mosquitoes, very common in WW1, less so in WW2. Malaria, sandfly fever and other diseases were, by the 1950s, brought well under control by modern drugs.

A tour of duty in Aden was normally two years, but by staffing Sharjah, Masirah and Riyan with unaccompanied and single airmen the tour at these stations was reduced to one year. Barrack blocks were mainly pre-war and wartime types and followed the usual design of wire screens over the window, electric punkahs and a high ceiling, with a wide veranda covered by the block or bungalow roof. On normal routine the erks were usually awakened around 0530-0600 with a cup of 'gunfire' by the cha wallah, had an early breakfast and on to work about 0700, to work through to about 1300 — times were dependent on area and time of the year (in winter many overseas stations went into UK blue uniform). When operations were on, they worked until at least dusk — and often beyond — to have the maximum number of aircraft available. For the next few hours/days squadron activity could be fast and furious as aircraft were refuelled, re-armed, checked and sent on their way. The ground crews felt they were participating and even the fierce heat and dust did not deter them.

RAF manpower in the Middle East was very thin on the ground; the withdrawals that went on throughout the area, as treaties were abrogated or different political parties gained power, had such an effect that for many years 8 Squadron was the only one for the whole area. A few squadrons in the Canal Zone were planned to reinforce any area should they be needed.

The handing over of RAF Habbaniya on 2 May 1955 to the Royal Iraq Air Force must have caused some regret to many of the thousands of tradesmen who had savoured its previously unheard-of comfort. Built at the then high cost of several million pounds in 1938 with expectation of a long tenure, the standards of overseas living on this station were among the best in the world. The RAF was allowed to maintain a staging post. This seemed to be a feature of RAF bases at this time — to put in a great deal of renovation and extension work and then hand it over to the country of origin. But at least Habbaniya had left its mark in aviation history by its determined defence against the besieging forces of Rashid Ali in April 1941 and its success in driving them off. After the end of the war and the rise of Arab nationalism, and despite treaties of occupation, its days were numbered: after the murder of King Feisal II and his Prime Minister in 1958, Britain was finally required, under Arab pressure, to abandon all its bases in Iraq.

Before that date, if one had to be posted overseas in that area, then this was the station to be. Every sport possible, including sand yacht racing and horse riding, was catered for, there were three churches, as many airmen's messes and dining halls, clubs of all kinds and entertainment. The station even had its own internal taxi service; it was also a Transport Command staging post, and could cope easily with three operational squadrons. Yes, a prototype indeed, but one which did not create others of its kind.

Along with this prestige station went the older stations of Basrah and Shaibah, both noted for their first world war and between wars history, nostalgic names to most airmen of the inter-war period.

Khormaksar in May 1958 was a hive of activity. To this vital staging post had come Corporal Counsell by Comet from RAF Lyneham, meeting on landing the 'solid' feel of hot air that greets all newcomers by air, who have not had the time to acclimatise that a troopship gives. The months of May and September are the worst months in Aden, due to hot winds being contained within the Tropic of Cancer; June, July and August are slightly better at 95°F (35°C). Cpl Counsell was put to work on the Transit Flight, virtually a staging post, working a 24-hour off, 24-hour on and 24-hour standby shift system. In addition to the increased flow of reinforcements and duty squadrons flying to the Middle and Far East, the ground staff handled much civilian airline charter traffic, some of it *en-route* to Woomera and Maralinga for A-bomb testing. The aircraft included Dan Air Yorks, Vikings, Tudors, Hermes, Canadian DC4M (an Argonaut with Merlin engines) the last carrying troops to Korea; Shackletons on the way to 37 Squadron at Aden, and even a French Air Force Junkers Ju52/3M. During the six months that Cpl Counsell was on the Flight the Kuwait crisis developed and 'all of a sudden it was Transport Command aircraft everywhere, shifting things with Khormaksar in the middle. At one time, out of a total strength of eight Comets, five were on their pans along with a dozen Hastings and six Beverleys. The shifts were now working 36 hours non-stop and had to be revised to 12 hours on, 24 hours off, during which you worked !! The tempo carried on for six months before it slackened off'.

During the Kuwait crisis of 1961 the conditions on the ground were at their worst: temperatures were around 120°F (49°C) and upwards, with blowing sand and high humidity. Servicing aircraft under these conditions could be very trying — in cockpits the temperature could reach 140°F (60°C) — and the old Vampire cockpit awning trick was adapted to Hunter and Meteor where possible. Sweat-producing activity was also reduced as much as possible. Aden has always been notorious for its wicked humidity.

On the North West Frontier of Pakistan and open desert airfields of Iraq, it was a recognised sport for local tribesmen to take pot shots at passing low-flying aircraft. In fact, there has been the odd death and injury from this, the best known being Sgt Fitter Elliot who had accompanied Sir Alan Cobham on his Australian flight and was killed by just such an incident over Iraq. This sport still continues and, although the construction and size of modern aircraft reduce the risk, a bullet in the wrong place on a heavy aircraft could be catastrophic. Sgt Roberts found evidence of this when refuelling a Beverley which had brought a construction party into RAF Salalah. A rifle-happy askari had put a bullet through a fuel tank and aileron control rod and out through the top surface of the wing. The damage to the spar web was repaired under conditions of some discomfort by patching with Chobert rivets and the pilot decided to take the aircraft to Khormaksar for repair to the fuel tank and the aileron control rod — which seemed to be taking an avoidable risk. Before he could do

Blackburn engineer Mr. Bill Bratton, weighs up the job of repairing a hole blown in the fuselage of a Beverley by an Arab time bomb whilst in flight from Kuwait to Bahrain in 1960. (W. Overton.)

so, Sgt Roberts insisted — rightly — that the F700 be annotated to this effect and signed by the pilot to absolve Sgt Roberts from any responsibility for possible further damage as a result of this rather strange decision.

At Khormaksar, Cpl Counsell was promoted to Sergeant and posted internally to Aircraft Servicing Flight (ASF) on second line servicing. ASF serviced the station aircraft, which included Shackletons, Beverleys, Valettas, Meteors and Sycamores. This work, despite the variety, was not strenuous in his new position, so he took over the Radio Bay, which was re-equipping to accept the Hunter FGA9. This proved to be most interesting as the equipment had to be installed and tested, stores demanded and so on. The work included radar gunsight ranging for the Hunter Aden guns, Rebecca Mk 8 and new IFF equipment. An interesting aspect of the new job was that all the radar bay fitters were National Service airmen who, previously deferred, had been conscripted as the scheme drew to its close. 'They were all whizz kids, average age 21-22 years old and the lowest qualification was an ONC, there were several HNCs, some in chemistry, and a couple of degrees.' The tour was marred by the death of a co-pilot who, returning in the dark along the fuselage boom of a stationary Beverley after doing pre-flight checks in the toilet area, opened a wrong door and fell through the hold on to the concrete apron.

To RAF Sharjah, off the Persian Gulf, one of the best known of overseas stations in pre-WW2 days, went Chief Tech Counsell as NCO i/c Electrical Test Equipment Bay, on a second, unaccompanied 13-month tour. To ensure that the gear was still within calibration, pieces were sent approximately 1000 miles every six months to RAF Akrotiri in Cyprus for major servicing, which just about allowed them time to get there, be serviced and returned; in general, though, the scheme worked. To Ch Tech Counsell the work was not demanding enough for a man who had no family to greet at the end of the day and he obtained a posting to 84 Squadron, operating Andovers. Before he started the new job, under the existing regulations he was able to fly home on a months' leave.

The new squadron job was as NCO i/c First Line Servicing for the Andovers flying support sorties for local operations, requiring a very early start of 0245 hours, and casevac work. The aircraft were usually away by 0300 and the bulk of the details finished by 0900. A shift system of 24 hours on, 24 off with every other weekend off was the routine and the work was hard, with some tension building up with so many people involved. This led to the airmen getting rather 'bolshie' and this was not helped by the tactless remarks of a Sqn Leader who, when escorting the visiting Under-Secretary of State for Air and after showing him, and dismissing, the First Line set-up, said 'Now we will go to Second Line where the real work is done!' Much restraint was needed by NCOs to cool down the First Line personnel. There are still individuals of the old school who, backed by the necessary uniform, can be as arrogant as pre-war officers.

Next to the Berlin Airlift, the withdrawal of the Aden garrison in November 1967 was the greatest in terms of time, people and material. The Aden Airlift was much more concentrated, taking only seven days to lift out 3700 people and hundreds of tons on material — and with no snags. For their part, most of the airmen were glad — Aden wasn't the most pleasant of places — and over the last 40 years of British control it had been the cockpit for numerous inter-tribal wars, and finally national in-fighting, in which the RAF had been directly involved.

The airmen's families were given three weeks to prepare for leaving; the organisation for doing so and getting all the families away was first class and reflected the hard work of the Movements staff. In fact, it was so good that some were sent to MQs on stations to which the husband was eventually to be posted when he returned to the UK. Others were delivered to MQs of their own choice and yet others to their own homes.

To the tradesman who helped load freighter or arm fighter, the political conflict was more personal. He was probably the head of one of the many families occupying MQ or hiring and knew that the risk to them was gradually becoming greater. At work he almost certainly put more effort than usual into his job in the hope that it might have some effect. But it was not to be and Britain soon faced up to make the decision that withdrawal was inevitable and politic. And so the airlift was put into motion, with complete success. As well as the direct action of those at Khormaksar the stations of M'hurraq and Masirah were directly involved in the moving of people from Aden, many of whom stopped there before going on to the UK.

After the Aden evacuation, selected squadrons and units were based on the two RAF stations on Bahrain Island, M'hurraq and Manama. The former developed into a large well-equipped station able to accept and

Night scene on the apron. Beverley aircraft on overnight stop while staging through RAF M'hurraq during 1967. Aircraft are marked Royal Air Force Middle East. (R. Honeybone.)

Loading a Scottish Aviation Pioneer into a Beverley. Note the Zip-Up staging folded and stowed in the port clamshell door. (W. Overton.)

service the largest and newest of the RAF's aircraft. Strategically, the island sat in the Persian Gulf just off the Saudi Arabian coast about 200 miles north-east of Qatar; defensively, it was surrounded by potential enemies, and at the mercy of the unstable politics of the day.

The stations endured much the same climatic conditions as Aden or Kuwait — heat, humidity and little shade — but the towns of Bahrain were nearby. In 1970 the island held a large number of assorted aircraft, including the Wessex helicopters and Andovers of Communication Search and Rescue (COMSAR) Squadron, one of the very few squadrons without a number. One technical view at the time held that the servicing of helicopters should be by qualified specialists. However, this idea faded as helicopters became more numerous and, when Chief Tech Turner joined it, the squadron had both specialists and non-specialists.

Sharing their hangar was a Royal Navy Wasp unit, with whom there was the better kind of service rivalry. The period was that of the great RN recruiting campaign headed by the words 'Fly Navy': posters and stickers were everywhere, exhorting all who could to do just that. The matelots (or fisheads as they were inelegantly called) saw the joke when one of their Wasps went off with 12 inch high fluorescent orange letters under the fuselage, urging all to 'Sail RAF'. The Navy were amused.

In its early days, when a Wessex became due for a major inspection it was sent to the UK. Harry Turner and friends, in preparing a Wessex for transport to the UK by a Belfast, did so to a sequence. They removed blades, tail pylon and rotor head, fitted a skid to the fuselage, deflated the tyres and oleo legs to allow the Wessex to sink onto the skid and removed the oleo legs. The Loadmaster of the Belfast had the rear doors open, ramp down, and rollers in position and down to the tarmac. All components were stored in the Belfast. The Wessex was hooked to a powered winch and the Loadmaster operated the winch to drag in the Wessex. Unfortunately,

on one occasion the winch failed and, on putting it in neutral, 'that Wessex shot backwards down the ramp and flopped onto the ground. We jacked it up, put more rollers under it and washed our hands of the whole affair by going to tea. I suppose it went into the Belfast eventually but we didn't want to know'.

The Beverley was really the first of the big British transport aircraft and was unique in its ability to lift enormous loads out of small, rough airfields and in being not just a 'furniture van' but an essential strategic aircraft, capable of dropping up to 90 paratroops. Its variety of freight extended to whatever could be fitted into the vast hold. As a consequence, it was very often overworked, as in Aden by the army, with the result that, gradually, unserviceability increased. The ground crew detachments on these campaigns worked just as magnificently as the aircraft performed, but the Beverley air and ground crews often had a rough time. Where punitive operations were in progress, the aircraft was much in demand to carry heavy equipment and troops into the operational area and occasionally to drop paratroops. The Army had never had such a useful 'furniture van' before, and come to that, neither had the RAF, so there was the normal tendency to abuse its abilities by constantly requiring it to do jobs that were rather unnecessary. Also, there were the usual changes of mind to complicate matters.

The overall result was that the ground crew and their helpers would load a Beverley and then a change of order would require an unload, both of men and material. This, on a hot and humid strip, with sand and dust blowing, temperatures well over the 100°F (39°C) and no shade did not make for friendly co-operation. To put the work into perspective, albeit in a humorous way, Chief Tech Gerry Hatt, who was then a Flight Engineer on the aircraft, was often called upon to perform tasks beyond the servicing schedule, which he did. But in the doing it sometimes created excessive strain on both air and ground crews. So Gerry Hatt was moved to write *The Billtong Song* (to the tune of

Clementine), which sums it all up very neatly:

There's inertia south of Persia
At Azaibah something's wrong.
Whilst at Sharjah, bumf looms larger
But the Bevs are pressing on.

In a freight bay in dispersal
Figured out by swearing Sarge
There's a trim sheet, it's a grim sheet,
With a payload much too large

Force Commander takes a gander
Then remarks with British phlegm
'Don't shut the door yet, she'll take more yet
We'll re-write the ODM'.

Fill the boom with sweating bodies
All with sick bags pre-arranged
'Ere she roars off, take the doors off
Kick 'em out, it's all been changed.'

On the flight deck, airborne light check
Being done with greatest care,
Sixty paras dive like 'arrers'
Ninety miles from anywhere.

Now it's over we're in clover
No more freight or bods to move
Britain conquers, let's get 'Honkers'
By the way, what did we prove?

Mau Mau disputes in Kenya arose from long-standing beliefs by the Kikuyu that their lands in the White Highlands of Kenya had been stolen from them by white settlers. In fact, most had actually been purchased by legitimate deeds of sale, but quite a lot by the shady 'clever white trader, ignorant native' approach. The Kikuyu, the tribe most involved, finally revolted in 1952 in the most unpleasant way, killing and mutilating isolated farmers and families, with the result that opposition was immediately organised. First moves were on a police action basis but the quick escalation of violence created the need for British troops and, to support and assist, the RAF.

The RAF begun its part by flying in troops in Transport Command Hastings and Valettas. The service was quickly involved but, with the steady rundown that had taken place since the war, had very few aircraft in Kenya, all of which were based on RAF Eastleigh. A former nice little posting to that most pleasant station, servicing one Proctor, two Ansons and a Valetta, was about to be rudely shattered by the arrival of Hastings, Valettas and Dakotas of the support force. In addition, to cope with the increased demand for reconnaissance, casevac and leaflet dropping, the RAF HQ utilised a Police Reserve Air Wing of private light aircraft and raised it to the status of an RAF unit. RAF HQ also formed 1340 Flight with Harvards modified to carry one .303 front machine gun and light series bomb racks: the Flight arrived in Eastleigh in March 1953.

A flying problem that had an effect on the ground crews was the altitude of the Highlands which, at around 4,000 ft (1219km), restricted the load that could be carried because of the effect on engine power, making it necessary to carry out more sorties with consequent increased workload and wear and tear. The larger Transport Command aircraft were more suitable and economical in practice with smaller loads, but they were restricted in their manoeuvrability when dropping supplies into confined areas. A number of airstrips were brought into use and erks on these exercises had the doubtful pleasure of looking over their shoulder for Mau Mau while servicing the Harvards, light Cessnas and Tripacers. The Harvards were useful for strike attacks and did a first-class job, their fire and bomb power being more than supplemented by the typical Harvard howl! What RAF tradesman hearing that noise for the first time hasn't been startled? It would terrify most uninitiated British let alone the Kikuyu. Perhaps that was the secret.

To move the increasing army reinforcements Yorks, Hermes and Argonauts were also used and this period of September/October 1953 proved the busiest for the station personnel. The 1,300 troops with their hundreds of tons of equipment and supplies lifted out in 41 aircraft created a high work-load, not least to 'Works and Bricks' who were at full stretch repairing the damage to the natural runway caused by the airlift, which was further exacerbated by Vampires of 8 Squadron called in from Aden. Finally, four Lincolns arrived from Bomber Command to carry out heavy bombing attacks on the Mau Mau strongholds.

The advent of the Lincolns with their large bomb capacity helped considerably. The intensity of their attacks finally began the process of surrender of the terrorists. To the armourers involved the work output can be gained by figures given in Air Chief Marshal Sir David Lee's excellent book *Flight from the Middle East*. In September 1954, 214 Squadron dropped 2,000 500lb (226 kg) bombs, fired 77,000 rounds of 20mm ammo in 160 day and 17 night sorties, which meant a lot of humping of bombs and reloading of guns. The task of bringing heavy ammunition from ship to main supply point, and then to user unit via a dump, is a heavy one, involving much security and skilful MT operation. In between, the armourers will have handled this dead weight several times and carried out many storage and safety checks. Although every attempt will have been made to keep the storage area cool (easier in Kenya) this is not always possible and the work is always hot and sweaty. One rarely sees a fat armourer. The service police will probably have provided escorts to the convoy, checked routes and co-ordinated the whole movement, a more interesting facet of their work. With the conditions prevailing during this emergency all ranks would be armed.

Here is probably the right place in this account to give some prominence to the most sought-after tradesman in hot war situations — the armourer — who gained considerable experience in both hot and cold war situations.

After WW2, new weapons developed with more emphasis on electrical operation, and then armourers moved into the missile era, with its attendant electronics, so the trade had to be arranged to suit. From this requirement evolved the present Aircraft Engineering Technician (Weapons) and Mechanic. The trade was further subdivided into three groups: aircraft armament installations; weapons preparation and generation; and small arms and ground defence weapons.

At the end of WW2 the armourer was versed in all types of 'iron' bombs up to the Grand Slam, rocket projectiles, all types of machine guns, anti-personnel bombs and a selected few had a knowledge of weapons not even in service. Through technical development and conflicts like Korea and Vietnam, a number of weapons have evolved which appear to break all the internationally recognised codes of decency in war, if such emotions can still be accepted. They include defoliating chemicals, the napalm bomb, laser-guided bombs, fragmentation bombs, ballistic missiles and the other goodies that civilised man produces to settle his differences. The politician makes the decision, and man has come a long way with a microchip now operating his club. The Armament trade, as a result, is now as highly technological as any in the RAF and well merits its own Trade Group.

A few years after the start of the Malaya Emergency it was decided that the best form of attack against the terrorists was to use 1,000 lb (454 kg), 500 lb (227 kg) and fragmentation bombs in large numbers, together with rocket, cannon and machine-gun attacks from strike fighters. To be able to service properly the ever-expanding range of offensive weapons necessitated more specialists. The trade at the beginning of WW2 had covered all weapons; after the war it comprised Armourer and Fitter Armourer, who both did all that was necessary to store and fuse bombs, bomb-up aircraft, maintain gear and bombsights, service gun armament, align sights and service synchro gear, service all hand guns, rifles and machine-guns, service turrets, arm grenades and take men on to the range for shooting practice. This was done by the two grades, which in essence meant that the Armourer was normally on the Flights and Gunnery ranges, with the Fitter Armourer in charge or on dumps, workshops or Maintenance Units.

As armaments increased in size, complexity and variety under the impetus of forced

Bombing up and servicing a Canberra B2 for real in Malta during the Suez operations against Egypt in October 1956. (MOD.)

development the trade has been made more specialised by dividing the armourer trade — first into two groups, gun and bomb, which eased the problem somewhat but both groups had their work cut out to cope. Manipulating up to twenty 1,000 lb bombs into the bomb bay of a Lancaster was gut work, despite the lifting gear designed for the job. Likewise, a fast turnround of a squadron of fighters each carrying eight 60 lb (27 kg) rockets needed stamina. In the crises of Malaya, Suez and Aden the aircraft were armed in conditions sometimes of extreme discomfort; similarly on Malta and Cyprus the full-scale war loads of the squadrons assembled for the Suez operation and, in Aden, the hot dusty winds and corrosive humidity did not make for an easy time.

Probably the pinnacle of the armourer's art was during the period of Thor and today, to a lesser degree, the Bloodhound and Rapier. The first is now history but the other two are still active; both had many 'black boxes', or trays, of changeable circuitry, requiring the services of a qualified electronic tradesman but there was still plenty left for the armament group. And behind all this sophistication is the bread and butter work of maintaining the personal arms of the station: rifles, hand guns, machine-guns and, for the RAF Regiment who have their own armourers, the mortars, light field weapons and Rapier, a rugged but still sophisticated ground-to-air missile.

Following pressure from Egypt, Britain agreed to evacuate her forces and the squadrons and units in the Canal Zone were

Large bombs on trolley, strong man required. Bombing up Canberra B2 of No. 100 Squadron, RAF Wittering. (C. C. Cole.)

airlifted out, the last airfield to be evacuated being Abu Sueir in April 1956. Egypt took over the Suez Canal on 26 July 1956. Britain and France intervened in the subsequent hostilities between Egypt and Israel and finally issued an ultimatum for both countries to withdraw 10 miles (16 km) each side of the canal. Israel did so, but Egypt did not, and at 1615 hours on 31 October 1956 Britain and France attacked the Egyptian airfields. The stated objects of the invasion were to: bring about cessation of hostilities between Egypt and Israel; interpose Allied forces between the two countries; and safeguard the canal by occupying Port Said, Ismailia and Suez.

Bombing was carried on for two days to neutralise the Egyptian Air Force and an airborne assault was made on 3 November. On 6 November a cease fire was ordered and a United Nations peace-keeping force took over. One military aspect that pleased RAF bomb-aimers was that they were so accurate that the local civilians living near targets were not injured and had complete faith in Britain's pledge not to bomb civilian areas. The build-up of squadrons engaged had taken place on Cyprus and Malta, giving the personnel of those bases a lot of hard work but also a sense of participation. For the squadron airmen, many a senior must have wondered if they were heading for another Canal Zone tour. After the decision to pull out, under pressure from the USA, the participating aircraft were assembled on Malta, for the last leg of their return to the UK, and on Cyprus, the original jumping-off base for the attack. The two forces soon dispersed, beginning with the Cyprus force. Shackletons of 203 Squadron were employed in shunting 30 tired ground crew at a time from Cyprus into Luqa, Hal Far and Ta Kali to service the second force.

Malta itself was soon to be in the headlines when, just after Christmas 1971, Mr. Mintoff, the Prime Minister, ordered all British troops to leave by the first week of January 1972. Short notice indeed, but the RAF were equal to the occasion, possible as a result of early intelligence. Married families were a high priority, but first all serviceable aircraft were flown off. Ground crews were given a choice of posting in the UK, but Senior Tech Jim Hughes, who was in the midst of all this, was unlucky with his. One effect of the postings was that 'the scattering of highly trained Nimrod personnel to other units was hardly conducive to efficiency'. This comment illustrates a much-condemned feature of RAF life — the scattering of trained personnel.

Those who were left in Malta after the initial evacuation, mostly SNCOs and airmen, got down to dismantling everything RAF. Hughes cleared out libraries, churches and chapels, packing up serviceable items for transfer to the UK and mostly destroying all

RAF VC10 of Transport Command ferries out service familes from Malta in November 1967 from RAF Luqa. 5,000 wives and children were flown out. (Bruce Robertson collection.)

traces of RAF presence. 'Probably the most interesting job was the removal of large quantities of ammunition from a huge dump in a natural cave in the centre of the island. This consisted largely of 500 lb (227 kg) bombs which, because of a ban on the use of

Harrier ready to be towed from its hide for a sortie after being serviced in Belize. 1979. (MoD)

Valetta harbour, had to be carried in three-tonners across the island to the old seaplane slips at Kalafrana. There they drove onto flat barges and floated out to the freighter. Rumours had it that these bombs eventually ended up in Vietnam where the Yanks were short of 'iron bombs' at the time. The armourers in charge assured us that the bombs were safe but when one rolled off a truck new sprint records were established. When winter storms struck the island and the bombs had to be dumped from Hal Far airfield, the sight of lightning striking all round them was even more terrifying.'

A feature that struck Hughes during this period was that the job of cleaning up had been left entirely to the Flt Sgt in charge of Aircraft Servicing Flight and his NCOs. Surely not a new feature! A few weeks after, Malta allowed the RAF to re-occupy the island but the RAF eventually left this uneasy area — this George Cross Island — in 1979.

Cyprus had been involved from 1953 to 1956 in the wave of terrorism/nationalism— sometimes the dividing line is rather blurred — that was sweeping the Middle East and Cyprus's own brand, EOKA, had begun to attack British servicemen and installations from 1953. The army, which bore the brunt of the policing, called in the RAF as their operations dictated. For the airmen, it was mostly the inconvenience of being confined to a closely guarded airfield or unit, with any local excursions strictly under guard. The aspect of airfield defence was carefully carried out by the airmen themselves, with professional assistance from the RAF Regiment and the army.

In Korea from 1950 until 1953, Nos 88, 205 and 209 Squadrons operated Sunderlands on anti-shipping duties and flew 1647 sorties. One of these useful aircraft brought a doctor to HMS *Amethyst,* landing under fire on the Yangtse river. Korea showed up the deficiencies of age of Britain's fighter aircraft which were outmatched technically, though not tactically, by the Russian MiG 15s. The American Mustang performed particularly well. The lessons learned were incorporated into the next generation of jet fighters.

One posting overseas that was refreshingly different was to Belize, a small pro-Western country that borders Guatemala. Because of aggressive noises from Guatemala, who wished to take over Belize, that country asked for British assistance in November 1975 (Britain had flown supplies into Belize following a devastating hurricane in November 1961) and half a dozen Harriers were stationed there — and still are in 1985 — to keep a watchful eye along the border. This one regular station in the Americas makes the posting unique, but the work follows the pattern of so many of the RAF's involvements.

When the Falklands crisis exploded into hot war, the RAF was required to operate in a new and hitherto unexpected role. The air war (except for some RAF Harriers operating from the Navy carriers) was to rely on successful operations over distances longer than had been thought possible. The key was air-to-air refuelling.

The Falklands gave the RAF just as many problems as the other services, mostly caused by the inordinately long ranges required of both bombing and supply aircraft from the main base at Wideawake airfield on Ascension Island, which was the nearest (and only) base that the RAF could use. The island was 4260 miles (6856 km) from the UK and it was nearly as far again to Stanley and the hot war. Range of the current aircraft precluded non-stop flight without refuelling and one of the first objectives was to get tanker aircraft to Wideawake. Supply aircraft were also wanted, to be ready to take supplies to Stanley after victory was gained. Very few fully converted tankers were available and civilian contractors and RAF Lyneham had priority in fitting refuelling probes and receivers to Hercules, Nimrods and Vulcans. The last two were modified by the manufacturers and the Hercules by RAF Lyneham and Marshalls Ltd, which meant overtime for the airframe trades.

On Wideawake, conditions were fast, furious, dusty and crowded. Most aircraft had flown long distances and required AAR to get there; some had been ferried by sea. The

Concentration of aircraft on RAF Wideawake, Ascension Island, during the Falklands campaign. Among the aircraft are Victor tankers, Hercules transport, Fleet Air Arm/Royal Navy Harriers, a Nimrod AEW, a Vulcan and Chinook. About 26 aircraft can be seen. 1982. (MOD.)

decision had been made to send Vulcans in the tactical operational role to bomb Stanley airfield. Servicing of all types of aircraft had to be done just as efficiently as on the more fully-equipped home bases, and with the Vulcans there was the added specialist job of loading the bombs and setting up the aircraft for their accurate delivery. The build-up of aircraft on the island was rapid and caused great congestion of machine and manpower on an airfield that previously had coped with no more than about six aircraft movements a week. Fortunately the USAF had developed the airfield to take Galaxy C5s, so plenty of tarmac area was available, and the station was also used as a missile space tracking station, so communication facilities were first class. The erks were housed in tents hastily erected

in a village with the picturesque name of Two Boats; food and equipment was flown out but, because of the priority demands on aircraft stowage space, was insufficient at first. Life was Spartan but the weather was good!

When it was decided to bomb Stanley airfield, two Vulcans were put on standby, first doing their work-up in the UK and being fitted with flight refuelling gear. For the technical support of the 50 Squadron aircraft, a team was flown out with the necessary ground equipment. The Vulcan team, with whom was ASC Chief Technician Len Develin, were issued with one camp bed, a sleeping bag, two plates, a set of cutlery and a plastic mug, and had to find their billet in the warm darkness at Two Boats, about eight

XW 598, one of the Vulcan aircraft that carried out the long range bombing of Stanley airfield on the Falklands. Possible AAM racks under the starboard wing. (L. Devlin.)

miles away. Accommodation was in eight-man tents. The Vulcans had arrived after a nine-hour flight with the aid of AAR and were promptly gone over with the proverbial fine technical tooth comb.

The momentous day started with the exciting order 'Prepare your aircraft from lunchtime'. The team went into action, and 'it was with an air of trepidation surrounding our detachment that we saw our crews arrive and climb aboard. In my job I deal with aircrew all the time and they were naturally tense. The flight line became all noise as the Victors started up along with our Vulcan. Being dark, with a starlit sky, one's feelings became one of pride. To see all the planning of weeks come to fruition and to actually be involved in this historic occasion is hard to put into words, but the whole detachment felt proud . . . Even at this time we could only speculate where the Vulcan was to unleash its bombs. The aircraft streamed off and eventually the dusty airfield was quiet.

'In due course the Victors started to recover as they each off-loaded their fuel. As the hours went by, we began to realise that the mission was complete and the time of landing of our Vulcan and its last supporting Victor was announced. We thought we would celebrate the safe return of our Vulcan with a beer or two on landing. The crews would be thirsty; liquid aboard a Vulcan is taken sparsely, no bathrooms aboard. The day wore on, the airfield still a hive of activity, and we were ready and waiting with the beer on ice, and by late afternoon two tiny specks appeared and got larger, two ageing warplanes coming home. A sense of pride once more came upon us. We were glad to see the safe return of our aircraft; 16 hours flying in a Vulcan had not happened for 15 years or more. It landed and taxied in. All and sundry came to greet the returning crews and the beer was accepted with relish. Whilst all this ballyhoo was going on, we serviced the aircraft and put it to bed for the night.

'. . . After we had tucked the ageing lady up for the night from the first sortie and all the aircrew were gone, we found quite a few cans left and who should arrive from their day's efforts but a platoon of Marines awaiting their chopper ride back to the ship, moored off the island. They looked hot, dusty and thirsty. "Would you like a beer?" we ask. Well, after gaining permission from their NCOs (very proper in the Marines) they accepted a beer. It was an interesting interlude, you gain quite an insight into people's attitudes to jobs over a beer. These Marines were just raring to go and get stuck in. A sudden hustle and bustle, then they all lined up and doubled off to the war zone . . .'.

The Nimrod was as vital to the success of the campaign as was the Harrier, the sole Chinook, or the Hercules. The vast amount of information it could collect by its sophisticated equipment and feed direct to Naval and Air Commanders in the UK and off Stanley gave the Task Force leaders a superior edge in the operation. Because of its great importance and the risk of enemy interference, the aircraft were fitted with Sidewinder AAMs to defend themselves; and to give them an offensive capability, if an opportunity was presented, they also carried the new Stingray air-launched torpedo and Harpoon anti-ship missile. Their ground staff contained, as may be expected, a high proportion of electronic (air and ground)

Electronic engineering air communications technicians carrying out major servicing to a Nimrod at RAF Kinloss. (MOD.)

The arrival of Harriers from HMS Hermes into Port Stanley after the ending of hostilities in the Falklands 1982. Typical winter. (MOD.)

trades to maintain the mass of sensitive electronic equipment at a high state of readiness — which kept them up late at nights.

It might be debatable to say that of all the RAF trades, the ones that have advanced the most in technical content are those of electrics, electronics and telecommunications. Between them they maintain and control the very heart of the systems upon which modern warfare depends; radar screens, missile interception and control, computers, communication systems — the full list would take half a page. But almost everyone will agree that the trade is vital and there can be little doubt that there are many systems under wraps which depend on their expertise. Imagine a modern fighter service without radar, advanced navigational aids, electronic counter-measures, the tracking of missiles, computer-controlled systems — the airmen's pay would be at risk here — even down to control of electric systems on ground and air equipment. And the telex/telephone would be missed.

It is accepted that all trades are important and interlock, but the jigsaw picture presented can be seen much more clearly with the aid of key pieces. For instance, the Nimrod is literally packed with sophisticated equipment upon which the fate of the country could well depend; it does more than just accompany fishing and naval vessels. And there are the new satellite communication systems upon which the modern services are increasingly dependent. New computers are being introduced for sector operational centre bunkers, each has more computing capacity than the whole system they are replacing. Modern missiles depend on electronic control; low level contour-ranging aircraft depend on the radar map navigation instrumentation to keep the aeroplanes constantly on course and height; and the long range air supply route to Ascension and the Falklands depend on electric operation of navigation systems and AAR interception. And so it goes on.

All the above equipment requires high quality servicing to maintain its advanced abilities, and this in turn has required greater knowledge of the tradesmen. As in all aircraft trades there can be no errors in workmanship; too much depends on efficient operation of aircraft, engine, systems, armaments, communication and navigation. One begins to perceive how vital is the job of any specialist ground trade, man or woman, and how important are the back-up trades in supporting them.

The base on Ascension Island was soon settled and into the routine of priorities. For tanker squadron personnel it was 24-hour maintenance and servicing; for bomber units, the armament personnel had the physical work of loading the Vulcans, which was critical. As the campaign developed, specialist equipment was flown out and fitted into the operational aircraft; this included radar, new forms of armament and other secret stores.

Although the campaign in the air was primarily a Royal Navy and Fleet Air Arm conflict so far as 'hot' sorties were concerned, the part played by the erks on Wideawake

Airfield was the vital one of supply and support from the most distant base ever used in modern warfare. Where the action was, the RAF was represented by the essential tradesmen on the carrier HMS *Hermes* with the RAF Harriers, and also aboard vessels carrying other Harriers and helicopters. Wideawake was aptly named so far as the service was concerned; those there sometimes had difficulty remaining in that state with the long hours they worked maintaining base and aircraft.

Obviously, all ground crew concerned in the Task Force wanted to be in the action but it wasn't quite that kind of war; it was more under the control of the Navy, which in turn was dependent on Nimrod and Harrier for survival, and on the supplies from Wideawake. One cannot choose who worked the hardest or performed the most important

Suppliers and Movement personnel working in the Supply Control and Accounting Flight at RAF Finningley, March 1985. (Cpl Marion Hamilton WRAF, RAF Official.)

task. All worked to the maximum and every job was dependent on another. The Victor tanker crews were interlocked with the successful Vulcan attacks, the vital Nimrod reconnaissance flights, receiving aircraft from the UK and assisting Harrier and Hercules on to Stanley in the closing days of the war. They slogged, with the MT, to bring up stores from the Ascension port to create dumps of ammo and fuel for the tankers. Catering staff formerly coasting nicely on stations at home were now performing culinary miracles and feeding healthy, work-hungry men on a diet which would be Savoy Hotel standard to WW2 tradesmen in a similar position. The admin trades excelled themselves in the rapid conversion and build-up of Two Boats, the RAF accommodation village.

Two trades that came in with a bang on this operation were those of Supplier 2 and Movement Controller. The flow of supplies and the movement of personnel were the two major streams and they had to be co-ordinated by their respective trades. That there were no bottlenecks of any consequence speaks volumes for the logistics of the campaign; the supply of manpower was somewhat restricted until there was somewhere to go; that required the superb

Army regiments and the Marines to take the Falklands with the aid of the fighting matelot, a job which they did admirably.

The inevitable casualties received the full benefits of helicopters, ships and VC 10 back-up. The dedicated skills of the RAF Nursing Service ensured that having been evacuated via helicopter to the hospital ships and then on to Uruguay, they would, after treatment, be flown 7,000 miles direct to the UK. That was one exercise the VC 10 ground crews were proud of.

The RAF was tested more thoroughly in the Falklands than in its previous campaigns, mainly because it was operating at very great distances from home but also because it faced an enemy air force that pressed home its attacks, a situation not known since 1945. All the previous crises had been against less than third-class opposition. A modern first-class air power would be a different gaggle of geese again, and it is for this contingency — by participation in NATO — that the RAF planners have worked so hard; to introduce modern aircraft of all types, which perform better than the anticipated adversary; and progressively to provide efficient servicing systems for them.

Chapter 5
New Aircraft and Planned Servicing

At the war's end, thousands of aircraft were parked on airfields around the country waiting to be reduced to scrap — for example 1000 at RAF Hawarden, 1200 plus at High Ercall, 500 plus at Hooton Park, 350 plus at Little Rissington. The sight of these brand-new aeroplanes being dismantled by the saw, axe and crushing machine raised the inevitable 'Why?'. The reason was that the lessons of WW1 had been learned: the aircraft industry was not going to be starved of orders through a large number of cheap aeroplanes being available to whoever wanted them. Some selected aircraft were, however, overhauled and refurbished for our allies' use,

for example Harvards for the French Air Force.

In 1946, RAF Hawarden was one of the airfields used as storage for hundreds of 'new and unused' aircraft whose eventual fate was to be the aviation equivalent of the knacker's yard. On this station and on others, until the knackers set up shop, the airmen were employed in keeping records: collecting engine numbers, component numbers, checking this and that to keep them gainfully employed. Hawarden stored mostly Wellingtons, built at the adjacent Vickers plant and with only their test flying time, along with the odd hundred or so Martinets,

That's your lot! Beverley WH116 being broken up at RAF Seletar, January 1968. (W. Overton.)

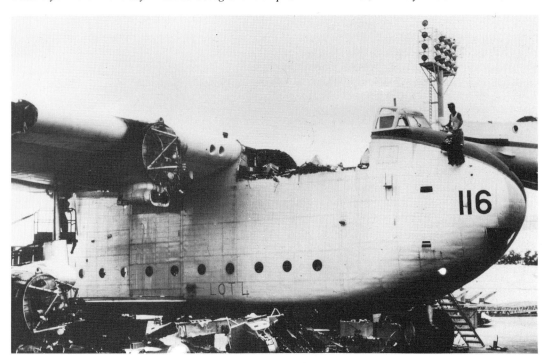

Masters, Warwicks, Ansons and Halifaxes, so there was no lacking in variety.

The same scrap procedures applied to engines and tens of thousands were disposed of. Although the major manufacturers were still mainly concerned with their latest piston engines, the scrapping of previous orders did at least ensure that they, like the airframe makers would not be starved of future orders. However, one major manufacturer, Rolls-Royce, had done considerable development and produced — for the Meteor — the engine of the future, which was to place Britain at the forefront of engine technology. They had put their faith and vast resources behind an almost unknown RAF officer in the fight to build the revolutionary engine.

Aviation was brought into being by a succession of dedicated inventors with, usually, an engineering background. Their names are known to any student of aviation history and many of them became builders of aircraft in the mass. Flg Off (later Air Cdre Sir Frank) Whittle was from the same mould: an inventive genius who triggered off the post-war generations of jet propelled, high

Working on the Derwent engines of a Meteor 8 at RAF Stradishall in May 1954. Note old style toolbags and care of the highly aerodynamic wing skin surface! (RAF Official.)

Electricians carrying out a test check on the Goblin engine of a Vampire TII of RAF Stradishall in May 1954. (RAF Official.)

performance aircraft. With a degree of backing by the Air Staff and a long, often depressing and disappointing development, the engine was eventually produced. It was not the first, that was made by Germany, but the Whittle was built by Rolls-Royce and with that winning combination it was able to be developed and go into production and power Britain's first jet aircraft. The engine was not a war winner as such, for the Meteor, the first operational aircraft powered by the Whittle engine, did not come into service until the war was practically won. The main contribution of the jet engine was in the rebuilding of post-war air forces, of both allies and former enemies.

In 1946 the De Havilland Vampire joined the Meteor in service; on the drawing board was the first jet bomber, the English Electric Canberra and, a close secret, DH was planning to build the world's first jet airliner.

Fortunately, the Meteor, the Vampire and its derivative the Venom, were good aeroplanes and more than proved their worth on the rough airfields and dusty heat of Aden and over the jungles of Kenya and Malaya. In Korea the first real lesson of having inferior aircraft was pointed. Although the myth of the MiG was punctured by top class flying of excellent late-type piston engined fighters, the need to re-equip with modern jets was made painfully clear: the development of types in prototype form was accelerated and the new types still on the drawing boards were modified by the lessons learned.

When the RAF began to rebuild, it naturally wished to re-equip with new jet aircraft and, just as naturally, the politicians decided the need was not valid. In this case they had a point, for first consideration was to get the country back to peacetime operation and production. So the RAF used WW2 aircraft, with the Meteor and Vampire equipping some of the fighter squadrons at home. These two aircraft were technologically advanced enough to require manufacturers' courses for the relevant tradesmen, although service courses were soon instituted, notably the Meteor course at RAF Cosford.

These two jet fighters were operated against the background problems of rapid loss of manpower, ageing WW2 aircraft, too high a proportion of NSA with a consequent dilution of technical skills, increasing independence of Commonwealth countries causing the loss of bases, political unrest in areas in which the RAF was seriously undermanned with operational units, and the outbreak of several serious campaigns and police actions, which required more manpower and aircraft.

The introduction of the jet brought its own particular problems to the ground crew. The basic services of the first jets were fairly standard in pneumatics, hydraulics, armament and control systems. The main difference was, naturally, in the engine, which brilliant designers and engineers had developed from Whittle's original engine to a reliable engine with vast potential. At first the method of operation and starting could be dangerous, with spilt kerosene prone to igniting, or the vacuum cleaner effect of standing too close to the air intakes or the high speed exhaust. To protect people from the suction effect of the intake a safety mesh

was at first installed; to protect the ears from the high pitched scream of the early DH Goblins, earguards were eventually made available.

From the ground crew angle the problems lay mainly in servicing and maintaining aircraft performance in the rough and tumble of squadron flying at home and overseas. First among the requirements was the need to maintain the ultra smooth outer surfaces to retain the efficient aerodynamics on which to some extent the aircraft's superior performance depended. This, initially, meant continuous polishing. Another problem was that engineering tolerances were so much finer. And as successive new jet types were introduced so they brought more advanced systems, instrumentation and radio/radar communications.

Another new aircraft should not be forgotten — the Sikorsky Hoverfly II, which entered RAF service in 1946 with 657 (AOP) Squadron and was a type every bit as revolutionary as the jet but in a different sphere. The helicopter, the 'chopper', had reached the end of its long gestation and the tremendous potential seen for it by its designers — and eventually the Air Staff planners — began to be realised. The Hoverfly II (actually the Sikorsky R-6A) began the long story of helicopter success which is still unfolding.

The Hoverfly was superseded by the Westland series beginning with the Dragonfly (formerly the Sikorsky S51), built under licence by Westland who went on to build several successful designs based on Sikorsky helicopters. Other types entered service, for example the Bristol series, and in all cases their impact on tactical planning was immense. Among the wide variety of roles they could undertake was casevac, supply and rescue (their paramount job) and, moving away from the humane work for which they ideally suited, they are now being increasingly used in the attack mode as gunships. These aircraft also brought their own particular problems, mainly with the engine transmission to main and tail rotors and the settings of the rotors. The ground handling too was different. Helicopters equip all search and rescue squadrons and many an unfortunate person, or a silly one, has heard the phwop-phwop of the rotor with great relief. The maximum lifting ability of these remarkable aeroplanes has advanced tremendously.

The year 1951 was the beginning of a decade that was to bring to fruition the Air Staff's plans for the long term rebuild of the post-war RAF. Within that decade came the new jet generation, which was to bring the RAF once more to the forefront of military aviation as an air force to be respected for its technical innovations. The Hunter (1954), Jet Provost (1955), the first of the V bombers, the Valiant (1955), and the Javelin (1956), followed by the Vulcan and the Victor (both 1957) were all aircraft that advanced service aviation by many years — and that includes the superb engines that powered them. Equally they advanced the standards of technical servicing and maintenance requirements. This the RAF had prepared for by first instituting manufacturers' courses attended by specially selected tradesmen, who were chosen not only for their ability to assimilate the latest 'gen' but also for their ability in passing on the information to their fellow tradesmen back on their units. Full information on the aircraft was quickly absorbed into the syllabuses of technical training schools.

However, a number of British government ministers did not show the inspiration and foresight which, presumably, had been the reasons for their election. Certainly not the Secretary of State for Air in 1957: Duncan Sandys introduced the White Paper on Defence in which he stated that the missile would supersede the manned bomber. As a result of this blinkered view and later financial cutbacks the Avro 730 Mach 2 bomber, the Hawker P1121 strike fighter, the Saro 177 jet/rocket fighter, the Fairey fighter and the Rotodyne, a helicopter version of the Beverley and, worst of all, the TSR2, surely one of the most advanced aircraft in the world, were all cancelled. An order for the American swing-wing F1-11 was

subsequently also cancelled. These so-called short term economic solutions gave birth to long term problems. The missile theory was an example: it lasted for a few short years, was scrapped and the strategic role of the manned bomber re-instituted with the V bombers.

During the early part of WW2 an unacceptably high percentage of operational aircraft was out of action each day on servicing, maintenance and repair by methods which were proving inadequate. The causes were quickly perceived and rectified by introducing specialist Servicing Flights into the squadrons. As the name implies, the Flight's duty was to service those aircraft beyond the technical capacity of the operational Flights of the squadron. In large units such as Flying Schools the same procedure applied but on a Servicing Squadron basis.

When the Servicing Flight scheme was introduced into operational units there was some initial opposition, mainly from Fighter units who had become attached to particular aircraft. This was understandable but was overcome. The old method tied up tradesmen and, more importantly in war, no immediate replacement for the unserviceable aircraft was guaranteed. Under the revised system, as soon as an aircraft went into Servicing Flight it was taken off charge of the holding Flight, which then took on charge a serviceable aircraft from the Servicing Flight. The same procedure was applied for an aircraft going into a Maintenance Unit (MU).

The system was a great improvement and was generally in use throughout the war. Towards the war's end, however, when operational flying had increased intensively and more technically superior aircraft were in service, the system tended to become overloaded, particularly on MUs which had, in addition to Inspections, all major aircraft repairs within their region to do. A problem of spares also bedevilled the units. When a spare was not immediately available there had been the accepted routine of 'borrowing' a spare from an aircraft which was temporarily U/S, categorising the U/S aeroplane as 'Aircraft on Ground' (AOG) until the spare arrived and thus producing the well-known 'Christmas Tree'. The demands of war magnified the problem and often the supply of some spares would be unable to meet the demand.

Often, an Engineer WO or Flt Sgt would bring an aircraft on inspection early or late on the plus or minus of the 10% leeway allowed in flying hours in order to try and regulate an orderly flow through the hangar for his available tradesmen. The airmen would carry out the work according to the inspection sheet. By mid-inspection the aircraft would be surrounded by the debris of dismantled cowlings and panels, tool kits and boxes, airlines, electrical leads and oil containers of various kinds. On some well-run squadrons much of this would be in suitable racks; on others . . .

An example of one of the most successful of the garage — or should it be flowline? — systems was the Base Servicing Party at RAF Pembroke Dock in 1941 under Sqn Ldr W. Hicks MBE. Here, Sunderland major overhauls were carried out on aircraft that were operationally sited around the world — and they were completed in 10 days. The scheme was successful because of good planning and the holding of a good stock of spares liable to be required. The planning centred on the method of carrying out the overhaul. When the aircraft arrived in the hangar it was stripped by several small gangs of tradesmen, each under a junior NCO, who were detailed to a specific section of the aeroplane — wings, tail, engines, hull, radio gear, armament, electrical etc. Much time was saved by the substitution of major assemblies

A typical pre-Planned Servicing scene – to a Hunter – prior to the introduction of that scheme with its attendant order and equipment designed for faster turnround. June 1955 at RAF Leuchars. (Bruce Robertson collection.)

such as tanks, engines, propellers, radio gear, those off the aircraft being fed into its relevant section for servicing. Each gang serviced its own section or system of the aircraft and then re-assembled it. The items exhanged were serviced under ideal conditions and placed back into stores for re-issue on later aircraft.

The last of the WW2 designs — DH Hornet, Hawker Tempest and Fury, Supermarine Spitfire, Bristol Brigand and Avro Lincoln — were ageing fast against the jet newcomers and although quite acceptable for the kinds of operation for which the RAF had so far used them in Malaya, Aden and Kenya, they would find the fighter opposition of a great power perhaps too formidable, excellent aircraft though they were. Their servicing and maintenance had followed the conventional lines of WW2, although the first application of the Planned Flying and Servicing scheme was beginning to cut servicing times. Also, in accordance with the political demands, numbers of fighter squadrons were being disbanded, and the periods of service of their tradesmen were coming to an end. The RAF was steadily losing these war-trained men who had turned smoothly to the next generation of aircraft, assisted by updated literature and manufacturers' and revised courses in training schools.

The next logical, and most important, step was the study of time taken by tradesmen to do the actual servicing tasks and find the causes of hold-ups. Work study teams were formed to cover all servicing operations where it was considered time, and thereby money, could hopefully be saved. This field of application had been used with considerable success, particularly after the Benson Experiment of 1954

The introduction of Planned Servicing had been preceded by a period of intense statistical analysis when squadrons and units were subjected to a flow of forms, several of which had to be completed in detail each day on the flying and servicing of aircraft, MT and equipment. The two best known to NCO tradesmen were Stat 1 and 2. Most NCOs had the pleasure, or otherwise, of compiling these. Stat 1 was a daily form, usually kept with each F700, which recorded the aircraft's daily activity in terms of flying hours and serviceability and manhours required for a particular task. Stat 2 was a weekly form and covered a Flight or Section's aircraft and equipment and was much more comprehensive in its requirements. The extra

Planned Servicing being carried out on a Meteor NF XI at RAF Stradishall 10th May 1955, showing newly introduced control cabin on right. (Bruce Robertson collection.)

paperwork, plus wall charts and other recording required, meant a lot of extra work — especially for the NCO i/c Flight or Section. It also had the effect of throwing up paper-minded NCOs who were in their element at the desk rather than in the hangar or on the apron; many were promoted on this particular ability.

For a few years the statisticians held sway while the new scheme was evaluated. Although all this was probably necessary, the old problem of spares availability was still the critical factor and this was improved only slowly. The statistical analyses and subsequent deliberations resulted in the present trend towards control rooms, computer cards, and the analytical control of practically every operation that requires man or woman power.

The concept of Planned Servicing, integrated with Planned Flying, was based on a paper by Wg Cdr E. A. Harrop, a brilliant engineer who commanded the Servicing Squadron at RAF Fayid in 1948. The paper was detailed, imaginative and long-awaited. It foresaw, and proposed measures to overcome, problems of rapidly shrinking manpower being utilised to service aircraft designed to a high technological standard, without requiring a mass of complex ground equipment, except at base depots. It aimed constructive suggestions at the aircraft and equipment maker for the design of new aircraft with fast turnround capabilities. This latter requirement has always been a top priority although sometimes not carried out to the letter of the contract, especially under the stress of quick replacement of new types during wars. The American designers were very good in this aspect.

The whole essence of Planned Servicing was that all servicing was timed in relation to a 24-hour clock, with each sequence of operations so timed that a tradesman was able to carry out his sequence without another tradesman overlapping or obstructing him.

Air Electronic aircrew at their posts in a BAe Nimrod AEW-16. Photograph shows well, not the equipment but the spacious conditions. (Marconi Avionics).

This particularly applied where congestion could slow down work, as in the cockpit or cabin, undercarriage wheel bays, rear fuselage, wing interiors etc. The system made each area available to each tradesmen during the period and so speeded up the overall turnround time by the team. All operations were controlled by a SNCO from a mobile cabin where servicing cards were issued and progress charts maintained during the servicing period. The whole scheme was related mainly to the Inspection Schedules but could be, and was, adapted to repair schemes.

Initially, the application of the scheme caused some disruption, because it required clerks specially trained in the Kardex visible-edge system on which the servicing records were based. For the Command NCO, when the charts arrived, along with a mobile cabin, clock and the new clerks at HQ, this was new ground indeed. At the beginning, the time taken to keep up-to-date a system more complex than the one it replaced cancelled out the time gained from the faster turnround; and, of course, it needed extra personnel — the clerks. But the system was modified as experience was gained and soon it became standard procedure, not only for aircraft but for transport, ground equipment and specialist equipment. The overall saving in time was as much as eight days for a Lancaster.

In flying units, the standard form of technical control incorporating the visible-edge system was introduced in March 1952, and special teams visited units to show, by setting up sample systems, how it worked. After the trained clerks had settled down, Planned Servicing became a compact system that could be easily moved with the unit. The Kardex system was popular throughout its period of use; eventually it became a much modified scheme that employed computers.

The modern method of aircraft servicing can be likened to a production flow line but using time and space rather than units of assembly. On the production line, the components feed to a line, which itself is moving. When servicing an aircraft the different trades (components) move to a stationary unit (the aircraft). Like the flow line the whole system depends for its efficiency on timing, with each operator performing a definite function. The cockpit, or cabin, offers an example. It is usually a confined area in which are many components that require servicing. Wg Cdr Harrop's Planned Servicing concept ensured that under a rigidly controlled time schedule only one or two tradesmen at the most were allowed to work in the cabin at the same time. This means that they entered the area with all necessary tools and a worksheet detailing all the operations required to carry out their particular task. They were allowed only the time indicated on the work progress card and the NCO i/c the servicing team had this under his control.

At the end of the allotted period the particular tradesmen vacates the aircraft cabin to allow a different tradesman to carry on. This system is carried out all over the aircraft and by means of progress and disposition charts the NCO i/c controls his team throughout the time scale laid down. An absolute necessity for efficient operation is that the hangar or workshop must be fully equipped with every possible aid to make the task easier, that all tradesmen are fully trained, and that inspection schedules are correctly itemised and broken down into steps. Each aircraft servicing team is answerable to, and controlled by, a central control room that has the necessary charts for manpower, component lives, graphs and aircraft state board.

The original Planned Servicing idea of allowing only one trade in one place at one time was modified, based on the experience of SNCOs on the type. The NCO in charge now controls his team without the aid of the clock system, switching any man to another job if the first, original, detail is found to be occupied already by another body. Every inspection schedule is broken down to various minimum tasks, each task printed on a card with details of the job, time allowed, tools, materials and equipment required.

The successful operation of Planned

Servicing made planned flying possible. As an aircraft became U/S, because its inspection was due or from faults brought about by the stress of maximum flying, it was replaced by an aircraft from the servicing stream. In its turn it would be allocated a bay fully equipped with all services needed — air, hydraulic, oil, electricity etc. — and with all the necessary tools and equipment. The servicing system ensured that the aircraft was in the bay for the minimum time and that there was a constant standby of aircraft to feed the flying squadrons.

A major contributory factor to unnecessary complexity of servicing was the lack of standardisation of aircraft equipment and systems, a point which Wg Cdr Harrop made in his paper. Instead of fitting, say, one or at most two hydraulic systems, preferably by a specialist manufacturer, many systems were used: Messier, Vickers, Fairey, Dowty, De Havilland, Short, Handley Page, etc. The saving in servicing time on specialised equipment would have been considerable. Standardisation came closer with pneumatics, for practically all British aircraft used Dunlop air-operated brakes.

Also frustrating was the then British design fixation of apparently not laying out system equipment in a planned or logical manner; for example, appearing to fit items where a bit of space presented itself, causing pipes to be bent at all conceivable angles, which made each pipe a one-off. American aircraft were exceptionally good in this respect, all pipes neatly grouped and logically laid out along the shortest route, all items accessible wherever possible. But one of the greatest eye-openers to British operators was the first view of an American maintenance manual. They were a mechanic's dream, making ours appear dry as dust. Their presentation of servicing operations used step-by-step photographs, which even their thickest mechanic could understand.

When a new aircraft is introduced, the

Fitting two tailplane, port and starboard to a Phantom of Squadron. Note that the white inner circle of the roundel and the white strip of the fin flash is now deleted. 1984. (MOD)

Two Aircraft Technicians Airframe working on the cockpit of a Phantom. The AAR refuelling probe is seen on the left. 1984. (MOD.)

service part of its design philosophy will be influenced by the need for planned servicing with estimated turnround times. Part of the acceptance trials will be devoted to this aspect. If accepted, an aircraft will be taken over by an evaluation team and every servicing operation will be monitored, analysed and progressed by teams of specialists until an efficient cycle of work is evolved and the equipment needed is supplied. All the data is correlated, fed back to the manufacturers and modifications are raised as required. Since the introduction of this scheme, tremendous progress has been made in this important aspect of design: as a result, overall turnround time of servicing aircraft has been reduced.

A £15M Tornado on operations cannot be allowed to spend unnecessary time unserviceable on the ground. That single aircraft is capable of doing as much damage as several full squadrons of the heavy bombers of WW2; any future war is likely to be based on split-second timing with maximum utilisation and every available

aircraft will have to be employed. The cost of these highly efficient machines has risen at the same rate as their destructive efficiency and both are contributory factors to their reduced numbers in the RAF. Because they require the most sophisticated equipment (itself designed to perform complex tasks as simply as possible), this complexity of aircraft and equipment, together with the necessary specialist tradesmen and their requirements, means that for full efficiency the aircraft must be housed in modern hangars in the rear areas and be close to specialist supply lines. And yet, paradoxically, the aircraft are also required to operate under forward field conditions, in most weathers with the minimum of servicing and using the minimum of equipment. The balancing of these conflicting operational requirements is just one of the headaches a good designer has to accept and, in most cases, to overcome. It is problems like this that Planned Servicing is designed to ease.

The Air Publications (APs) necessary for servicing a modern aeroplane have become almost as sophisticated as the aircraft. The first organised layout was a three-volume scheme; Volume 1 was a description of the aircraft, Volumes 2 and 3 were divided into parts. In 1947 a Volume 4 was introduced and in 1948 the scheme was expanded to six volumes. In addition to this six-volume scheme, associated equipment and procedures were covered in 1954 by another dozen. Since that date there has been considerable revision of all documentation of aircraft and their systems. For instance, the present Form 700 Servicing Record is far more of a detailed record than ever the old blue covered form was. It is now laid out in a four-ring binder to allow daily changes of rectification and servicing sheets, which are sent to Technical Control for evaluation, recording and finally for entry into a computer to provide the statistics necessary to today's RAF.

One branch of servicing that developed from the conjunction of necessity and manpower shortage was in so-called Composite Trades, which means that certain grades are taught to carry out simple servicing tasks of other trades in addition to their own. This concept is not new, having evolved during WW2 from practical experience in Malta during its siege, AOP squadrons operating from forward airstrips, the Refuel and Re-arm parties of the desert and Burma, and as far back as 1940 with the Servicing Flights that were raised as mobile back-up units in France. The best-known, properly trained, force of this type within the RAF was the Servicing Commandos who were raised in 1943 to do a similar job to the Servicing Flights of 1940 but who were trained to fight as well as to service aircraft. They were closely behind the invading troops in order to get selected airfields and airstrips ready just as soon as it was reasonably safe. For WW2 the composite trade idea of the servicing commandos required a selected volunteer with the right quality and approach. He was taught to carry out servicing, mainly of any Allied fighter that needed it, in all the basic trades of electrical, instruments, engine and airframe, to refuel and re-arm with rockets

and machine-gun and cannon ammunition, to do simple repairs quickly within his own trade and, with the team, to bring the aircraft up to Flight Readiness state.

There was no further need for this type of tradesman until the continuing decrease in trained manpower was reaching a state, in the late 1960s, that demanded greater utilisation of available trades. The need was more noticeable on First Line Servicing on units such as OCUs and FTSs, which often had up to 20 aircraft per squadron on the flight line. RAF Topcliffe, then the School of Air Engineers and Air Electronic Operators,

Author and F/Lt Bartholomew carrying out a F700 check prior to a flight from RAF Fayid in 1949. (Noble.)

introduced a system of Composite Servicing which covered Pre-flight, Between-flight and After-flight Servicing and the original servicing schedules were revised to retain all essential operations in a form that could be understood by tradesmen with a good basic engineering knowledge.

When the schedules had been analysed a detailed on-the-job training programme was devised. Chief Tech Honeybone, who was completely involved in this scheme from the beginning, said 'The prime consideration was motivation, as the tradesmen concerned had to accept the imposition of extra responsibilities without any increase in pay. Among the SNCOs had to be found those who could impart their specialised knowledge to junior airmen when the only reward appeared to be an increase in supervisory duties'.

Showing amount of ground equipment required to service a V-bomber (Vulcan) on the 'dock' principle. In addition a large amount of ground units are required. RAF St. Athan, January 1973. (Bruce Robertson collection.)

To assist technically some classroom tuition was given but most of the training was on the job, as and when convenient; if the aircraft were not airborne or during bad weather periods, for example. Chief Tech Honeybone again: 'Each airman underwent a minimum of training commensurate with his reaching a set standard in each subject, then a final check across the schedule was made by a Chief Technician as a "Passing out" control. The aim was to equip the airman to inspect items in the schedule to a "Serviceable to fly" standard; any question outside limits was always referred to the relative trade NCO for rectification.

'The "amateurs" tended to be more thorough than the "professionals", oil leaks sought out, tyres checked for damage with great enthusiasm and fuel dispensed in hundreds of gallons as the new mini-servicing chiefs got to grips as Composite Tradesmen. Each airman's Servicing Record was endorsed accordingly as he reached qualification standard. In a few months it was possible to effect the changeover to the new schedules without interference to the flying programme.'

With the engine and airframe trades the absorbing of electrical or armament trade knowledge appeared easier than *vice versa*. But with great satisfaction the School's manpower was able to work in a much more versatile manner with a consequent increase in utilisation. Morale improved and over- and under-utilisation was reduced and eventually eliminated, and fewer ground trades were needed for servicing, especially on detachment from base.

Perhaps one example that will suffice to show how the major servicing of a V bomber had reached a fine art under Planned Servicing is that given by ASC Turner. He had to take a Vulcan to 32 MU RAF St. Athan for a major inspection, to arrive at the hangar by 1030. He then went off to Control to debrief and complete the necessary documents. By 1200, when he returned to the hangar, the Vulcan had been washed, put into the hangar, jacked up, two engines removed, seats out and everyone hard at it. But Turner had his reservations. 'Scared me stiff, just like ants, but I query whether it was a good inspection. Too "screwed down" to inspect properly.' No doubt others will disagree. But such a vital aircraft could not, in those days, waste precious time in unserviceability.

Jet aircraft were becoming frighteningly expensive, a V bomber costing as much as £1.5M (1957 prices) off the shelf without equipment. They were large aircraft and brought their own problems, mainly in the equipment required for testing their advanced systems — the heavy and complex ground equipment. Their flying hours were also fully utilised with many long flights, a high proportion of which were overseas excercises, or showing the flag. The arrival of these sophisticated aircraft on an overseas station often posed the problem of its routine servicing by ground personnel unfamiliar with its intricacies, which was a factor in the Air Staff's decision to raise a new trade for ground crew, following the American concept of Crew Chief. The Aircraft Servicing Chief (ASC), was introduced under a 1954 Air Ministry Order (AMO) and specially selected Senior Technicians were sent on a short course to check their technical ability and then to the manufacturer. During these courses extra information was given on aircraft electrics, electronics and instrument equipment, to assist in assimilating the manufacturer's course. The selected airman had to have at least five years to serve after the courses and if he successfully achieved six months' trouble-free experience on the aircraft he was given accelerated promotion to Chief Technician. Although primarily meant for service on the V bombers the trade was used on other large — usually four-engined — aircraft such as the Beverley, Hastings, Hercules, Argosy, VC 10 and the Britannia, but sometimes under the nomenclature of engineer. The new trade had the effect of mopping up a few surplus Senior Techs, and a course for the V bomber ASCs was organised in 1954; parts of the course were at Vickers Armstrong Ltd, A. V. Roe or Handley Page and part at Melksham for basic electrical and instrument training.

An early course was attended by Senior Techs Harry Turner and Len Develin, trained for Vulcans; Gerry Hatt was a Beverley ASC, as was Bill Overton. Sen Tech Develin's course comprised a four weeks' airframe course for Aircraft Fitters (or four weeks on the Olympus for Engine Fitters) and included the relevant aircraft/engine systems. The two parallel courses then amalgamated for three months' basic aircraft electrics and general instruments, with an exam at end of each phase. The latter included navigation instruments. Both technicians' Vulcan courses were at that time held at the manufacturers' works at Woodford, Cheshire.

The trade requirements of a qualified ASC were truly tremendous and comprehensive, and a glance at the detail shows how highly trained he was. He was directly responsible for the servicing and maintenance of one very expensive aeroplane. In addition he was also responsible for its movement on the ground, other than under the control of the pilot, and, with the Air Quartermaster in the case of transport aircraft, the critical loading of the aircraft.

As a trained ASC he meets the aircraft on landing, gets technical reports from the captain and makes the necessary entries in the aircraft documents. He takes charge of the aircraft servicing team and ensures that servicing of the aircraft and ancillary equipment is properly and quickly carried out to the proper standards. Necessary technical publications, tools, equipment and spares are to be available. He directs and undertakes servicing tasks on airframe components, flying controls, engines, general instrumentation, cabin pressure system, fuel pressure, etc; carries out functional tests of armaments, radio equipment, the loading and unloading of missiles and ammunition, investigates defects and rectifies or arranges specialist servicing not included in his team. He supervises ground handling operations, marshalling, towing and picketing; ensures that all cabin and cockpit equipment, first aid, fire extinguishers, dinghies and emergency packs are properly stowed. He checks that cargo is properly loaded and secured, the aircraft is clean, sees that all service records of inspections, rectifications and replacement of components are recorded, and gives additional servicing or operational information; reports and records major defects and persistent minor defects for Second Line rectification. He directs ground crew, advises aircrew of the serviceability and modification state affecting the operational role of the aircraft. He reports to the captain on aircraft fitness for any operational role, and flies as observer on air test to note performance data.

He accompanies the aircraft into Second Line to advise on servicing and performance and any special checks which may be needed. On completion of Second Line servicing he assists in checks and functional tests of the aircraft and equipment. He takes part in air tests and completes flight reports where applicable. As Senior Tech Develin writes, 'a bit mind-boggling for some of us, but the idea was that on a technical de-brief after an aircraft had flown, the crew chief was conversant with the discussion going on around him. This still applies today.'

The hard grind of this job with its awesome responsibilities was compensated at times as Develin remarks: 'Over the years the aircraft have gone overseas to train crews on the low level routes of these countries. On these, and other flights away from the aircraft base, a crew chief was carried to service the aircraft on landing, and to prepare it for its next flight. This was the aspect of the job which appealed to most crew chiefs, with most job satisfaction gained and also to see parts of the world not normally visited by the British armed forces. The places visited sounded exotic, but often little was seen because of aircraft unserviceabilities. But over the years we have all seen parts of the world other people just dream about.' An interesting aspect of V bomber operations.

Another usually unpublicised trade, that of Electrician Ground, was involved in the electrical ground equipment required for Victor aircraft, in this case at 232 OCU at RAF Gaydon, which had Valiants and

Victors. The Mk 1 versions of these aircraft were both electrically started, the high power required being supplied from mobile starter trolleys, themselves actuated by diesel or petrol engines or electric motors. Because of the great power required from the starter trolleys and the possibility of one or more failing during a Red Alert exercise — or for real, because this was the era when the V bomber force was the first-line ultimate deterrent — plus the slowness in starting each engine, it was decided to invent a more foolproof starter especially for V bombers. The brilliant but simple solution was the Simm Starter Trolley.

This was a bomb trolley converted to carry 21 aircraft batteries with starter circuits built into them. Four heavy cables were plugged into the aircraft and the start was made from the external batteries. The idea was that all four engines could be run virtually together. It worked, if a count of five was made between pressing the start buttons. 'What a lot of batteries we used . . . if, as they usually did, they worked the aircraft could take off within 2-2½ minutes of engine start. The blokes on the Simm starter had to unplug the four cables and lock the panels in position before the aircraft moved. If it was an exercise — we never knew — the aircraft would go and if the cables weren't clear the Simm starter went with it, as once happened. The guy underneath needed to be strong, agile, accurate and very courageous.' So said Chief Tech Phil Brooks.

Another useful piece of equipment, developed to shave winter's snow off the faces of the runways, was a trailer on which was sideways mounted an operator and an elderly jet engine — believed to be a Derwent 2 with its jet directed downwards, in a fan-shaped outlet, to melt and blow away snow and ice. The trailer was towed by a Matador and the jets were throttle controlled so that a bit of extra jetstream to melt a tenacious patch of ice often resulted in the trailer beginning to taxi sideways! Later versions had two engines mounted fore and aft and were towed by a bowser which, because of the extra weight and stability and the opposing direction of the jet

The newest example of sophisticated technology still requires the application of basics to get it into the air. Tornados of the Tri-National Tornado Training Establishment at RAF Cottesmore in 1985. (Sgt. Brian Lawrence RAF Official).

The portable staging which could be dismantled and assembled, designed for the Beverley, but which was found to be unsuitable for overseas operations away from firm base airfields. This 'dock' tended to sink into sand under its own weight and was afterwards superseded by the Zip-Up staging that could be carried in one of the clam doors. (MOD.)

effluxes, was an improvement, but teamwork between bowser driver and jet operator was essential. It certainly saved a lot of shovel power.

The V bombers were always on show wherever they went and undoubtedly had a degree of glamour about them, if one can feel that way about an efficient machine designed

A Beverley, fitted with side movement skates (the nose can be seen jacked up on its skate) being moved sideways into the hangar, with tail well down to the clear the roof trusses.

(Ray Honeybone.)

to carry the nuclear bomb. But the transport aeroplane was the work-horse of the service and was required to go anywhere, subject to available landing and take-off aids, and carry anything, subject to its ability to fit into the holds.

The aircraft that proved the routes of Transport Command were the Hastings C1 and C2, which complemented the York and entered service in October 1948 in time to take a major part in the Berlin Airlift. The aircraft was based in the Middle East in 1950 and the Far East in 1957 and continued strategic operations on the routes until 1959 when, in turn, it was superseded by the Bristol Britannia, one of the best passenger and freight aircraft built. The heavy Hastings, powered by four Bristol 1675 hp Hercules 106 engines, performed extremely well and staging post personnel throughout the RAF world became accustomed to its peccadilloes (some mentioned by Bowers and Hughes) and were able to carry out an appreciable amount of work on it. As with all Transport Command aircraft, major inspections and rectifications were done at base. The Hastings' reliability became well-known and gratefully accepted, particularly in the middle of a hot humid night on a staging post where shift work was operated.

The Beverley, with its great size and height in wing and boom fuselage, required special ground equipment, most of which was almost as large and heavy as the aeroplane and, initially, not mobile. As far as its servicing was concerned, the Beverley had a few Sunderland-like design features, for example access ways behind the engines. To reach the great height, 'giraffe' type servicing platforms were designed, the first few mechanically operated — and not very successfully. When mechanical was succeeded by hydraulic operation, access was easier. This large aircraft was probably the first British design to use the 'dock' principle of servicing, whereby all the engines were surrounded by a built-up structure that contained its own ladders, storage bins and so on. But it was heavy and combersome and used only at base. For major access away from base a lightweight mobile, bolt-together structure was evolved, called the Zip Up. This proved ideal as it occupied only a little storage space in one of the aircraft's clamshell doors.

Because of the great height of the fins and rudders, the aircraft was a difficult machine to house, being able to use only the largest hangar and then only with the most careful handling by tractor driver and ground crew. Later, to facilitate ease of movement, side-tracking equipment became available. The use of this is well described in Bill Overton's book *The Beverley* from which permission has been given to quote the following extract:

'Soon after the Beverley came into service, side tracking equipment for hangaring the aeroplane became available. Since the wing span of the Beverley was substantially greater than the width of the doorway of the standard hangar, the side-tracking gear enabled the aircraft to be hangared sideways. Lack of headroom presented a further problem but this was overcome by raising the nose in order to

lower the fins to enable them to pass under the lowest parts of the hangar roof trusses. The aircraft was towed into position so that each set of main wheels mounted a low slung wheeled platform, the wheels of which were disposed at 180° to those of the aircraft. A trolley was then positioned under the nose and an electric motor (with a hand operated back-up gear) drove the elevating mechanism. With the aircraft now positioned in a nose-up attitude and with the main wheels on the side-tracking skates it was possible to tow it into the hangar. Once inside the hangar, the aircraft was positioned so that the fins were under the highest part of the roof trusses. The nose could then be lowered to the ground. Hangaring such a large aeroplane was a complicated procedure which demanded precision team work from all those involved in the operation.'

A skill that is often overlooked in the handling of the large and heavy aircraft is in their ground movement. This required the design and construction of new and powerful David Brown specialist tractors, a far cry from the old agricultural-type Fords and Cranes. These tractors are sophisticated in design and require specially trained MT drivers to move the multi-million pound aircraft.

The concept of air-to-air refuelling (AAR) as a means of extending the range of an aeroplane without reducing its payload in favour of extra tankage is not new. First experiments were carried out in America in early 1923, followed by the French in December 1923 and the British in February 1924. As was usual in those days, a long delay ensued — in this case seven years — between British experiments. Several methods were tried, with military application as their aim, before Sir Alan Cobham formed Flight Refuelling Ltd which, with Farnborough, carried out extensive trials on different methods and techniques with civil and service aircraft.

By the end of WW2 the operation of this

An MT prime mover/tractor designed specially for the moving of large aircraft. RAF Lyneham, 1980. (MOD.)

scheme had reached the point where it was planned to use AAR on bombing aircraft against Japan. The nuclear bomb stopped this. However, the idea was switched much later to Javelin and transport aircraft, and ground crews were required to modify a number of aircraft with sets of receiving and transmitting equipment. The AAR squadrons required a large fleet of tanker MT with extra drivers and, of course, a higher standard of specially trained fire fighters with all that fuel around.

The experiments were carried out in a desultory fashion and finally crystallised in the 'drogue and probe' method, which was tested by 214 Squadron with V bombers in 1958. Selected operational squadron aircraft were converted to receivers in 1960, mainly Vulcans with a few Victors. The Valiant had been converted successfully to the tanker role but main spar faults were discovered in 1964,

the aircraft was withdrawn from service and the Victor took its place. Other operational aeroplanes such as the Lightning, Harrier and Jaguar were modified for AAR and the Victor carried the latest three-point system.

Many long range proving flights were made with a variety of aircraft using a variation of the system, followed by regular exercises, but it was the hot war in the Falklands that finally pointed up its operational necessity. Usually a crew chief would fly in the large tanker aircraft and as a result many of these Chief Technicians would see much more of overseas than usual as individual aircraft were sent on an AAR exercise.

It may be conjectured from the previous description of the modern aircraft with their sophisticated systems, extremely powerful engines with high thrust, great fuel loads, carrying modern rocket missiles and in the case of the V bombers and transport aircraft,

In an attempt to reduce the economics of flying, the Folland Gnat light-fighter was developed but, although an order was placed, the RAF rejected the idea. However, it served as a two-seater trainer from February 1962 to May 1965 and then became famous to most people as the red painted Gnat of the 'Red Arrows'. In the photograph a Gnat Trainer is being towed by an 'agricultural' type tractor at possibly Central Flying School, RAF Little Rissington.
(Bruce Robertson Collection).

their great size, that the danger of accidents was an ever-present possibility for air and ground crew alike. And so it was.

Early accidents to the jet aircraft personnel soon alerted Flight Safety and ground engineering staff to the need to tighten up existing, and introduce new, safety regulations. When an aircraft is involved in an accident the public soon, invariably, get to know about it, especially when loss of life

occurs. Accidents to ground operating staff are rarely publicised because most of them happen on an RAF station, MT and Marine craft excepted. Fortunately, the very high safety standards in force have kept the accident rate down to probably the lowest of all the active air forces. Unfortunately, human error and occasional malfunctions of design decree that, however rigidly safety rules are enforced, accidents will happen. And

The Gloster Javelin, after clearing some teething troubles, entered RAF service in February 1956 to replace the Meteor and Vampire. It was a revolutionary design, being of delta-wing configuration and was employed in its designed role of all weather duties. Nine marks were produced for a total of 385 aircraft, which served until October 1964. This photograph of a F(AW) Mk. 1,2,4,5 or 6, is having its oxygen supply replenished, vital, for this aircraft often flew at 40,000 ft (12,190m) plus. Notice the exit/access ladder required for the pilot. (C. C. H. Cole).

in a fighting service acceptable risks must be taken.

The first accidents in the jet era were caused by the suction effect at the engine intake — often very nasty — and the high pressure efflux from tail pipes, this usually involving many bruises from being blown a few feet. Later, high thrust engines in aircraft like the Sabre, Phantom, Hunter and so on, ensured that being sucked into the intake meant sudden death. There have been very few.

The Heyford, Stirling, Sunderland, Lancaster, Bombay and Beverley class of aircraft introduced the risk of injury by falling on the concrete apron from a height during engine servicing; in the case of the Sunderland there was the possibility of drowning, and the design of an access to the rear of the engines has caused accidents. During arming and bombing-up in WW2 a quite disproportionate number of armourers, and adjacent other ranks, were killed by accidents occurring during this operation. Today accidents still happen and the air-to-air missiles are a new danger; in 1953 an airman got in the way of a 60 lb (27 kg) practice rocket inadvertently fired from a Hornet.

The pressure testing of cabins has been the cause of accidents, as when a valve has refused to operate and pressure has built up sufficiently to blow off a hatch. The high pressures involved in recharging oleo legs have also caused the odd accident by being overcharged. And on the explosive theme, the early days of ejector seats saw a few nasty accidents.

Towing the big aircraft has its small crop of marshalling accidents, for instance when voice communication is not enough, and a foreseen danger which has caused the NCO i/c to shout 'Brake!' has been heard by the towing tractor driver but not by the airman in the cabin. This problem has been solved by radio communication between all the marshalling team and specially built tractors. The use of radios had been extended to normal flight line operation. Usually a Corporal is in charge, communicating with the airmen marshallers and directly to the Flight Office for reporting any snags. Errors in movement by pilot or ground staff can result in expensive damage, but rarely injury.

There have been many airmen who have shown great bravery and initiative in moments of extreme danger and whose heroism has resulted in the saving of life. The deeds of helicopter aircrew are examples of the above qualities; when combined with a cool assessment of the situation they have resulted in many headline rescues and well-deserved awards. Away from aircraft operation, there have been many incidents and saving of life performed by RAF personnel in civilian backgrounds. Northern Ireland springs immediately to mind but brave deeds have occurred wherever the RAF — and the other services — have operated.

While all the assorted hardware was being dispensed during these years of peace and the service was beginning to re-equip, in a quiet (well, not so quiet) corner of Oxfordshire a small experiment was taking place which was to revolutionise the conditions of service of airmen and airwomen and to provide the coming all-professsional air force of tradesmen with a modern service, within which they could give of their best in the knowledge that their work was at last being given the status that had been lacking in the past.

Something has attracted the ground crew of a HS Hunter as the pilot gives some brief post-flight information to the WRAF ATC assistant at RAF Leuchars in July 1955.
(RAF Official.)

Chapter 6
The Benson Experiment — 1954

On 9 May 1957, during a speech in the House of Commons by the Secretary of State for Air on the Air Estimates, the public was given the first indication of an experiment that had been made, which he called the 'Personal Services Experiment' at RAF Benson, a station of Transport Command, to improve the conditions of other ranks. The following is the relevant extract from the speech, taken from Hansard Vol. 569 No. 105:

1. Much of our success in recruiting an all-Regular Air Force will depend upon trying to make life in the Service a little more agreeable. For this reason I should like to say something about the progress we have made in improving station administration as the result of the personal services experiment at the RAF station, Benson. The idea was to eliminate petty restrictions and to improve personal and domestic conditions.

2. We have been able to introduce many improvements and to remove many irksome restrictions. For example, airmen are now normally paid in their sections instead of at a central pay parade. Colour-hoisting by sections in rotation has been substituted for regular morning parades. There have been changes in such matters as arrivals and clearances, booking in and out, permanent passes, reporting sick, and drafting during week-ends. In the field of personal and domestic conditions we have had to take action to relieve congested accommodation, do away with double-tier bunks and speed up the dining service.

3. At a number of large stations officers have been appointed as families' agents. They handle all the needs and problems of married airmen and wives, arising from Service life. They have proved a success, and we have decided to introduce them generally.

4. There is no doubt that the general level of morale and contentment as well as the efficiency of a station can be raised without any adverse effect on discipline. I am confident that the action we have taken will bring benefits to the Service as a whole.

5. Besides trying to make life in the Service more agreeable, we must also see that both officers and airmen can enjoy a reasonably settled home life with their families in married quarters; and if they are posted abroad to a place where they cannot have their families with them, at least they must know that their families will not have to fend for themselves at home.

6. At the end of the war, we had 6,700 married quarters. Since then, we have built over 16,000 and nearly 3,000 more are under construction, both at home and overseas. During this financial year we expect to spend nearly £3½ million at home and rather over £1 million overseas. Generally speaking, we shall then have completed the bulk of the requirements.

7. There are, of course, some places overseas where it would be unreasonable to build because of local conditions. At the same time, there are a number of stations at home with married quarters, where our numerical needs have changed. Fortunately, these two difficulties offer a solution to each other. If officers or airmen are posted overseas and cannot take their families with them, we can offer them any excess married quarters on a

station at home. While we cannot house all the grass widows and their families, we can do a good deal to mitigate the discomforts and anxieties of members of the Service in this way.

8. However, it is not only for married men that we must provide adequate living conditions. The quality of our single accommodation has long left much to be desired and we devoted to its improvement as much of our resources as we reasonably can. In this year, we propose to spend upon domestic accommodation, other then married quarters, just over £5 million at home and £1½ million abroad.

9. To sum up, the Government's policy depends largely for its success on recruiting enough Regulars to get rid of National Service while keeping an Air Force of a size capable of fulfilling its many tasks at home and overseas. This can only be done in two ways: firstly, by the strictest possible economy in manpower; and, secondly, by making life in the Service as attractive as possible.

10. I have tried to show how we are tackling these two important problems.

In this speech the Secretary of State for Air was referring to a unique experiment, which had been carried out by Transport Command HQ over a period of 12 months from autumn 1953. Its origin had its roots in the recurring problem of poor recruiting against a background of near full employment with good wages in civilian life, coupled with a serious decline in the re-engagement rate of serving airmen, known as internal recruiting.

The consistent drop in internal recruiting figures over the years from 1946 was not just as a result of the RAF losing out in competition with pay rates in civilian industry; there was much evidence of other causes, accumulated (together with suggested solutions to the problem) by the Personnel staff of the Air Ministry and Home Command, and influenced by a Report from the Inspector General of Recruiting in 1952. Finally the Air Member for Personnel, Air

Chief Marshal Sir Francis Fogarty, decided to evaluate the more positive remedial measures put forward in the light of their cost-effectiveness, their relevance to the internal recruiting problem, some real improvements in conditions of service of other ranks and the advancement of their morale.

After discussions the AMP asked the AOC-in-C Transport Command, Air Marshal Sir Charles Guest, to prepare a plan for a Committee to test and evaluate the remedial suggestions, and to control an experimental investigation into improving airmen's conditions at a selected Transport Command station. The Command was chosen as a result of experience gained from the mounting and controlling of a successful experiment under Group Captain Slee at RAF Lyneham from August 1953 to January 1954, which had studied the utilisation of technical manpower with the aim of improving flying programmes. The experience gained from working with the Scientific Advisory Staff at Lyneham was important when the same organisation was invited to join this project.

Group Captain F. J. Manning, Senior Air Officer Administration, was given the Chair to plan, organise and control what became the Joint Experimental Steering Committee, with Sqn Ldr K. E. W. Pugh as his right-hand man, and they immediately commenced preliminary planning to produce by the end of 1953 an outline plan based on the following considerations:

1. RAF Benson was chosen (and gave its name to the experiment) because it
   (a) was set in average conditions of isolation,
   (b) was of permanent construction to normal peacetime standards,
   (c) had a fairly normal administrative structure.
2. Air Ministry Science 4, specialising in human relations, would participate and monitor the experiment
3. The Joint Steering Committee would be under the executive control and responsibility of Gp Capt Manning as Chairman. Responsible to him were:

118

Group Captain A. C. Dudgeon, Commanding Officer, RAF Benson;
Mr. P. Sudler;
The Inspector of RAF Recruiting; and
Group Captain Evel, Deputy Director AMP.

4. The experiment would be conducted in three stages, each of approximately two months, to evaluate;

Stage 1 — the elimination of petty restrictions

Stage 2 — the improvement in personal and domestic conditions

Stage 3 — a reorganisation of the station structure.

5. The aims of the Experiment would be:

(a) to test various changes in methods and conditions which appear to affect the efficiency, discipline and contentment at a typical RAF station;

(b) to ascertain to what extent any improvement in station efficiency, discipline and contentment is related to, and effects the attitudes of airmen towards, service in the Royal Air Force, and the desire to remain in it for longer term engagements or for a full career;

(c) to assess what positive, practical and proven measures can be introduced generally to eliminate known deterrents to internal recruiting for long term and pensionable engagements, and which will maintain or improve discipline and efficiency.

6. For the purpose of the experiment 'morale' was defined as 'The degree of satisfaction with, desire to continue in, and willingness to serve for the goals of a particular group or organisation'. These three elements were more briefly defined as 'The degree of identification' with a particular group or organisation.

7. The Committee would introduce any measure worth a trial, subject to the following limitations:

(a) any measure requiring long term and general adjustment to service conditions before introduction into the Experiment schedule.

(b) measures which would be too costly or requiring more time to assess then the Experiment schedule would permit.

The final Administrative Instructions, including all the main parameters, were drafted in the spring of 1954 by Sqn Ldr Pugh and copies distributed to all concerned, followed by essential pre-Stage 1 field work by Science 4 to sound out airmen's views on their current conditions of service. The idea was to evolve a form of morale measurement to check future attitudes that could be related to the results of changes in service conditions introduced during the three stages. Four other Transport Command stations — Abingdon, Dishforth, Hendon and Lyneham — were subject to similar measurements. The idea was that these stations would act as a control group for Science 4: conditions would not change here, so presumably morale would not change either. In addition, the Queen's Flight at RAF Benson was included in the early pre-experiment measurements because it was considered a high morale unit, and also, because they were one of the major reasons for the experiment, those other ranks of Transport Command who were re-engaging were interviewed.

After the preliminary measurements had been taken the Committee began Stage 1.

Stage 1: The axing of old traditions
(a) Guard duties

The airmen, when consulted, echoed the complaints that have long been made by the lower ranks to the effect that a mobile police patrol would be more efficient than one man on a rigidly defined beat, leaving wide gaps by which an intruder could enter. And there was the complaint that an airman would need rest after a night's guard duty, and that rest time would be lost to his section; many stations allowed a man detailed for guard also to leave work early to allow time to prepare. When changes were made to overcome these

119

complaints there was some temporary objections from the Corporals. They were required to carry on doing guard duties for a period after the airmen ceased doing so because extra RAF Police had not been drafted in early enough and the Corporals had not been informed.

(b) No more regular parades

It was definitely a way of service life — from 1918 — to attend morning parade and march to work, usually after an inspection and morning service. Now this time-honoured custom was to be eliminated and its loss caused no regrets whatsoever. The WOs and senior NCOs more than welcomed its removal, as this quote from a Technical Wing Warrant Officer makes clear:

'Well, we got more manhours out of them. They are at work at eight o'clock instead of losing the odd twenty minutes or so — it had a slight effect on their morale — I suppose you'd call it. It has pleased the airmen no end and it has pleased us as well.'

In trusting the men to make their own way to work they are treated as responsible adults, which of course they are.

(c) Revised colour hoisting parades

Instead of a full-scale flag hoisting parade with Squadrons and Flights in attendance, it was decided to reduce the parade to one representative section in turn, each section with its own officers and NCOs. The interest was maintained and a large number of airmen were made available for work much earlier. In effect it tied up with (b) above. Most airmen agreed it was a great improvement although, typically, some would prefer the parade to be abolished altogether. Again, see (b) above.

(d) Booking in and out ceases

One of the constant 'binds' of experienced airmen, this imposition was introduced well before WW2 along with its often accompanying humiliation of being treated as recruits by very young Acting Police Corporals, who checked airmen for smartness of person and clothing before allowing them out. It was eliminated with universal approval. However, this good idea was rather spoiled by the Station CO adding the qualification that this was a privilege, which would be withdrawn — for a fairly long period — from those airmen awarded 'Confined to Camp' (CC) punishment and Junior NCOs awarded reprimands. The first delighted reactions by airmen and JNCOs, who thought again that they were to be treated as adults, were rapidly negated by this qualification.

The CC itself was a two-edged punishment. In addition to being confined to camp many airmen felt that they could not relax until they had attended the 2100 parade at the guardroom, as failure to do so might mean further punishment. Many felt that doing the CC was expiation enough; to have the privilege of not booking out rescinded for a period three times the length of any CC awarded was indeed further punishment, and quite uncalled for. Many of the older, and quite responsible, men regarded this lack of trust as archaic.

(e) Sports afternoon revised

Perhaps one of the oldest customs in the RAF was the Wednesday afternoon sports period, based on the assumption that to 'play sport or watch it' out in the open was good for mind *and* body. The non-physical types were not taken into account. The practice, of course, was open to many abuses, primarily from NCOs i/c sections who had men working rather than playing/watching — unless the man was a member of the station's team, to whom all bowed the knee on fixture days.

Over a period of five months the attendance/non-attendance percentages were calculated, with almost always the largest figures being attained by the latter. Other 'minor' sports and so-called hobbies were included but, despite an analytical breakdown, it seemed that the hangar had priority (it proved it really) followed by the major sports of football, cricket, rugby, hockey, etc, This problem, if it was a problem, was partially solved by the introduction of the five-day week into those stations that could operate that way.

(f) Reporting sick

This was another oldie: reporting sick to the Orderly Sergeant or Corporal or to the guardroom at an unnecessarily early hour (0715 in the case of Benson) had been normal in the RAF. The team carried out an analysis on the theory 'that much apparently purely physical ill health has its origins in mental stresses' and divided the sickness rate into two groups, physical and psycho-social. Into the first they put all the 'normal' causes — geographical, sewerage, water supply, accommodation, food, hygiene, etc., and including winter flying. The second was subdivided into attitudes of authority and of airmen. Sickness at home bore no relationship to station life stresses or to malingering. The team altered the reporting sick time to 0800 at the Station Sick Quarters, which was unanimously approved.

(g) Fire piquet

Yet another oldie, from the days when domestic fire-fighting equipment was inadequate in an era of wooden domestic huts and buildings. Although rosters were issued from the SWO's office, during the war it was often a case of snap detailing by an NCO, irrespective of billet or station, unit or trade. There was usually a separate fire piquet hut in which the detailed slept at night, with the odd practice alarm. Training was primitive, mainly on available fire extinguishers, and an armband was worn. It was decided it would be better for the fire piquet to be detailed from each room or hut and the piquet would sleep in their own beds. The change created little impression.

At the end of Stage 1 the reaction measurement revealed no significant changes in the general level of contentment. However, in the long term practically all these changes came to stay and to be appreciated. The next stage of the experiment affected all other ranks and trades more personally.

Stage 2: Improvements in single and married conditions
Introduction

The practical tests carried out in this stage were, to quote the Report, based on 'the hypothesis that "the clothing, living and working conditions available to airmen and their families are thought to be below standards appropriate to the comparable civilian roles" and sought to improve the personal and domestic conditions of single and married airmen in married quarters'.

The 1950s were probably a very good time in which to conduct a scheme that got to the root of the matter as defined in the above paragraph. There was much discontent at the apparent lack of interest in the airmen's basic living conditions by authority; no obvious attempts had been made to improve conditions of clothing, accommodation, catering or married quarters since the end of the war and it was beginning to show in general discontent. It appeared that most of the Air Estimates were directed to aircraft and equipment and, essential as this was, little was left over for improving airmen's amenities.

Several group meetings arranged by Science 4 to check this aspect of contentment soon elicited a response which left no doubt how lower ranks felt about their status, and the reasons, before March 1954. The items actually introduced during Stage 2 were:

(a) New raincoats

Good uniforms, or the lack of them, was a subject with which all were in agreement. Various complaints included that the material was too thick and unsuitable on a hot day, and that they were never made to fit properly despite the camp tailors (or because of them). The men wanted the new T63 uniforms (of gabardine) and WRAF-type raincoats. The greatcoat came in for similar criticism. Unfortunately, the Committee could not do anything about this, but they managed to introduce a new type plastic mac.

Most airmen agreed that the mac was better than the old ground sheet, but the white semi-transparent appearance and material were disliked and caused a depressing effect on the level of contentment; the answers to a questionnaire on their use delivered an emphatic 81% against with 19% for, most people preferring the officer and WRAF type of raincoat. The macs were soon discontinued and eventually, along with the new T63 uniforms, sensible Raglan-style Burberries were issued throughout the service.

(b) Airmen's new furniture

On the question of single airman accommodation, all were agreed that the two-tier bunks were a waste of time. There was a valid reason of course: their initial introduction was at a time when wartime recruiting numbers far exceeded the capacity of barrack blocks built for a peacetime air force and pre-war huts laid down before this enormous increase of manpower. Their presence created overcrowding, to put it mildly; and the original 1938 barrack room designed to sleep 16 was more than doubled by replacing the single beds with two-tier bunks, and with four rooms per block that meant a lot of men using the toilets and facilities. And in 1954 the manpower of the RAF, although very low, was still well above the 1938 figure.

A spin-off from the crowded barrack rooms with their poor storage facilities was that JNCOs had very little privacy. One bunk was allotted per room for the NCO i/c that room to live in, but many JNCOs had to sleep in the rooms with the men — not the best way

Single airmen's quarters at RAF Finningley indicates how much progress has been made from the old dormitory days. RAF Finningley, April 1985. (RAF Official.)

of maintaining discipline — so their complaints were justified.

The new beds were well received but, to put this matter into perspective, many stations already had single accommodation and to many airmen this aspect of the trial was merely bringing Benson into line. The wooden lockers and wardrobes, although smaller in capacity than the old steel units, took up more space, but that was a design fault not the Committee's. On the result of the change a number of airmen were asked the question: 'In your barrack room do you think: (i) there are too many people (ii) there is about the right number of people?' The replies were: (i) 64% (ii) 36%.

It was considered by the airmen that the provision of decent furniture should have been done long before the Benson Experiment commenced. The Steering Committee agreed! To close the particular point the forceful comments of a Corporal illustrates the frustration of JNCOs at that time:

'I can't speak for myself because I am in a bunk of my own, but from the general Corporals' point of view it is terrible, is the accommodation, because they expect you to take charge of airmen, and treat them with some sort of — well, like a proper bastard, sometimes — and yet how can you do that when practically — I should say a good 80% of the Corporals are living in the billets with the airmen. They have to live with them, sometimes sleep above them, or under them.'

(c) Revised tool kits and new toolboxes

At work, the lack of spares for aircraft and equipment and suitable specialised tools had run like a thread through the fabric of the RAF since the days when airmen were forced to buy canvas in local bazaars to repair aircraft fabric, or when, in extreme cases, aircraft in India were forced to take off on the wheel rims because there were no tyres, or when Workshops had to make special tools. If this story of insufficient spares is ever told it will bring no glory to those concerned, be they politician, civil servant or Air Staff. It possibly still exists. Certainly it seemed a familiar theme at Benson whose technical tradesmen made their views known. Skilled men were stymied for the lack of tools as well as spares and some of the comments do not make comfortable reading so far as efficiency is concerned:

'This afternoon I wanted a screwdriver about three inches long. Well there isn't one in the tool kit. So that means I've to trot down the steps (servicing ladder) to the stores and wait behind a crowd of airmen before I can get that screwdriver. Whereas, had I had it in my kit — they are not expensive to make, they are about 6d (2½p) or 9d (4p) in Woolworths — had I had that screwdriver I could have had the job done, say, a good ten minutes or a quarter of an hour earlier. So a quarter of an hour was wasted by me larking about in the stores.'

Probably the Equipment Branch had their problems of supply — from the MUs and up the chain to the relevant Department in the Air Ministry or to the manufacturer. Whatever the reason the Experiment tried to tackle the problem at station level.

After the introduction of the new tool kits and boxes, the attitude of the majority was that they were still not adequate. It was found that the effect of the kits and boxes on contentment and efficiency was more difficult to assess. The choice of tools was welcomed by some, criticised by others (in this kind of project you cannot please all the people all of the time, but the experiment pleased most of the people). Efficiency was increased, of course, by having a more versatile range of tools, which meant less 'chasing around' and more time saved, but the team felt it was the outlook of the airman himself that finally decided the issue. Good quality tools would not necessarily make a better worker of one who did not wish to work and a poor tool kit could make a good worker lose interest.

(d) Goodbye to webbing equipment

The wearing of webbing equipment started in the mid-1920s; in their day they were accepted pieces of encumbrance but they had outlived their purpose, mainly because they had little place in a modern Air Force environment — although some station COs and AOCs did their best to retain them by having full monthly parades with all other ranks festooned in webbing in full marching order.

Before the Royal Navy introduced suitcases, the accepted RAF method was a kitbag to supplement the back pack of the webbing equipment, with another smaller kitbag if posted overseas. The Army, who used webbing equipment as a matter of routine, modified the kit bag by adding a hand grip. It was the advent of the Royal Navy's suitcase, and seeing Americans with their valises, that made airmen unhappy with this aspect of service life. There was, of course, the additional bind of cleaning the equipment and putting it on display.

There was no hesitiation by the Steering Committee in recommending that all webbing equipment, except the belt, bayonet frog and rifle sling, be withdrawn throughout the RAF, and this in due course was agreed. All this equipment found its way to a storage unit in the Midlands where it filled a large hangar, awaiting a purchaser from the international market.

(e) Introduction of a launderette

This item was strictly for the airmen's wives and therefore a new field in research of this kind. The long-lived lack of official interest in the needs of the wives in married quarters showed in the answers to a questionnaire about the launderette, even if the wives felt, on this issue, that there was no 'great need for them'. After a launderette had been provided the Committee asked:

(i) Have you used the launderette?
Yes 17 (22%)   No 62 (78%)

(ii) If not, do you intend to use it in future?
Yes 9 (14%)   No 36 (58%)
Don't know 17 (28%)

Those wives who did not intend use the launderette were asked to give their reasons. These were:

Had their own washing machines	5
Considered it too much trouble, or thought the launderette to be too far from the MQs	5
Considered it too expensive	4
Declared the machines did not work properly	4
Preferred to do their own washing	4
Needed to do a small amount of washing each day because of young children in the household	3
Had a preference for the local laundry	1

All the officers' wives interviewed had their own washing machines.

The Committee was well aware that the wife is a very important person with a great deal of influence on the husband's decision to continue in, or leave, the service and therefore should be given more consideration than hitherto. The next innovation shows that this concept had been well understood.

(f) Introduction of a Families Agent

This move was considered to be one of the most successful and far-reaching in the Experiment as a whole, and was welcomed by both the airman and his wife. But a job of this demanding nature required the personal qualities of firmness and tact, sympathy and understanding, patience and — very important — the ability to get things done, emphasising the great care needed to choose a man of the right personality, preferably a married RAF officer of some maturity.

The wives consulted were virtually all in favour of a Families Agent. They indicated their views on the subsequent questionnaire, which gave five possible responses to the idea:

		Numbers agreeing	
(i)	A very good idea	46	(71.8%)
(ii)	Quite a good idea	17	(26.6%)
(iii)	Rather a poor idea	0	
(iv)	A very poor idea	0	
(v)	Indifferent to the idea	1	(1.6%)

Previously, it was the individual airman and/or his wife who had to tackle any problem directly, and not always successfully,

and often with the feeling of being up against a system rather than a human being. The Families Agent acted as a buffer, took any load of anxiety from the airman and his wife and, eventually, by long association, got to know some of the personal problems of many of the married personnel. But it was this latter circumstance that was also the idea's weakest link. The RAF is a service of people continually on the move, the majority every two or three years, and a job of this nature requires stability. However, altogether the Agent was an excellent idea and was well received. When introduced to the service at home and overseas, at the end of the Experiment, the name was changed to Families Officer and it was not long before the Army and Navy recognised the need for their own Families Officers.

(g) A new NAAFI shop

Benson seems to have been both fortunately and unfortunately served: the station had a good modern NAAFI shop but it was staffed by some fairly poor counter assistants, judging from the uncomplimentary comments made by some wives who had waited up to an hour to be served by assistants apparently infected by the post-war 'couldn't care less' attitude. While almost certainly *not* typical, the attitude created a strong 'anti' feeling about the new shop which in itself was quite good, if pricey. After the wives expressed their appreciation of the shop, one typical comment was:

> 'Insufficient supervision by the Manager and his staff, who are often rude and bicker among themselves. Customers are expected — in fact told — to weigh their own potatoes, etc., an unheard thing in any shop in my experience. The time one has to wait is atrocious and could be improved if there were separate girls for each department.'

Because wives felt that they were treated as second-class citizens, all aspects of NAAFI shops were raised, with a recommendation, among others, that 'No matter how difficult the task may appear, it is essential that a really

This view of the small NAAFI shop within the Rose and Acorn Airmen's Club at RAF Finningley indicates the wide range of goods on sale for all ranks. March 1985.

(Cpl Marion Hamilton WRAF. RAF Official.)

determined effort should be made to impress upon all NAAFI staff that the service wife is entitled to the same consideration and respect as her counterpart in civilian life'. Shortly after this stage ended Benson was given a much better shop, and was privileged to have the first self-service one.

(h) Provision of garages

A measure of the increase in living standards is given by the increasing numbers of private motor vehicles. The 1950s marked the beginning of a change, when a vehicle was no longer considered a luxury but seen as a necessity, due to first class advertising by motor firms, full employment and the inconvenience of public transport. The airman was no exception to the trend and his

machines were beginning to litter RAF stations; the Experiment brought in the idea of providing weatherproof garages for cars and motor cycles, and was warmly welcomed.

In the first move only ten car garages could be provided and were allocated on a lottery basis at a charge of 2/6d (12½p) weekly. Because there was a greater number of motorbikes, proportionally, their garages, or shelters, were unfortunately sited at a considerable distance from the domestic site, which meant that they were not fully utilised. It was suggested that shelters be attached to barrack blocks. (In passing, it was the norm pre-war for a part of a hangar to be given over to the garaging of cars and motorcycles.)

Today, at all stations, vehicles are kept under control by providing car parks sited at suitable points on the station (sometimes even on the Square!) Servicing (DIY-style) is helped by setting up Motor Clubs.

(j) Improvement of children's facilities

A beginning was made by providing a playground and utilising whatever suitable material was at hand to excite children's imaginations, such as sand, car tyres, or an old car. On an RAF station there was also the possibility of old aircraft parts such as a cockpit (you can't start them off too young!). But a better idea was to employ an infant school teacher, which was warmly welcomed. However, this idea was peculiar to Benson and obviously could not be adopted universally.

(k) Improvements in catering

Service catering has always been the Aunt Sally for complaints, often with cause it must be said. Before Stage 2 got to work, it appeared that Benson's dining hall suffered from congestion and lengthy queues, despite meal times being staggered. The dining hall could not easily support the large establishment of airmen, and slow service resulted. Two legitimate complaints were that there was no separate dining space for JNCOs and airwomen, and that the provisions for disposing of scraps were extremely unpleasant (but good for pigs!).

To improve the situation, accommodation was enlarged by pinching half of the upper floor for use by JNCOs and airwomen, who were most grateful to have their own facilities at last. The layout of the main dining hall was modified by bricking up some entrances and fixing separate servery and guide rails to provide an easier flow of the queue. The previous complaint of food going cold by draughts was cured by this change and by the addition of extra hotplates. The 'dollop on a plate' system of serving vegetables was abolished by allowing airmen to help themselves (which created a saving). During meals the tables were cleaned and dirty plates collected on the cafeteria system by trollibar units; after-meals service was improved by new cutlery wash-ups. The change from the previous wall murals, which were eliminated by a redecoration programme, to a more austere style, met with a mixed reception, however.

Attempts were made to improve standards of messing but this again met with a mixed reception; some were in praise of better and more varied dishes, but others of the 'every Monday is fish and chip day' school did not appreciate the changes made. During the project there was in fact a slight but steady deterioration in the standards of catering despite the structural and organisational improvements, a view partially supported by the Benson catering officer, who put it down to 'loss of purchasing power due to rise in costs of such items as tea' and poor supervision by one NCO. The reader can make his own choice.

Today's standards, which Benson set off, are now extremely good as descriptions of meals at RAF Finningley in 1984 (Chapter 8) indicate. The extracts from the minutes of a Messing Committee of 1949 in Chapter 2 indicate how lax catering had become.

(l) Formation of a Women's Institute

A considerable amount of space was devoted in the Report to this project!

An airman's wife can be expected to have to change stations around every 2-4 years and for the quieter types it is always a daunting prospect to have to make new friends in different surroundings. For a woman raised in a town, the rural life can appear to be boring. There is a lack of social life which a Married Families Club cannot always fulfil and in the 1950s there were no disco clubs for the younger set. In a questionnaire asking whether the wife was a member of the Married Families Club, 19 out of 63 wives (30%) indicated they were, with 44 (70%) who were not. The reasons given were, briefly:

(i) the club opened only in the evenings, so young wives with children were not able to leave their quarters;

(ii) wives of aircrew who were away had a natural reluctance to visit a mixed club alone;

(iii) subscription rates too high;

(iv) drinking not liked by some wives;

(v) tendency for club to become exclusive to SNCOs;

(vi) officers' wives not eligible.

A Women's Institute appeared to have advantages that could overcome the Married Families Club criticisms and give the women a chance to organise among themselves. A first attempt to set up an Institute was vetoed by the Federation of Women's Institutes who could not allow one at Benson. After the Steering Committee indicated its wish, and in conjunction with 80 volunteers led by the Station Commander's wife as President, the Federation finally agreed and the project got successfully off the ground. The CO's wife gives a long but interesting account of their efforts.

Despite the success of the scheme it does not appear to have caught on for most stations. But it was an excellent move which greatly increased contentment level of the wives and so directly to their husbands.

Stage 3: Formation of cohesive groups

(a) Introduction

The changes in this stage, aimed at improving the efficiency and organisation of the station by unity of groups, were:

(i) A station reorganisation to intensify command and efficiency at Squadron, Flight and Section levels, to foster a closer officer/man relationship at section level and to encourage ideas to improve station administration;

(ii) Re-organisation of the pay parade;

(iii) Introducing marginal changes in Technical and Flying Wings to reduce servicing manpower per flying hour and increase aircraft utilisation

(iv) Improving the trade training of airmen and airwomen

(b) Station reorganisation

Science 4 based the proposed reorganisation of RAF Benson on a 'functional hypothesis': the influence on morale of positive knowledge by the airmen of their position in a chain and why; that that chain must relate to all working and non-working activities; and that they should know the relationship of their chain to other chains and how the overall organisation operates. They should have a clear understanding of the composition and function of the chain. Science 4 saw it as important that the organisation within the chain should issue clear executive instructions which could be seen to relate to the overall function of improving morale. A high degree of failure in this respect would probably result in a lack of good morale.

Before the reorganisation, Benson was, in effect, composed of a number of different working units, some functioning independently of other groups. Overall, the organisation appeared disjointed and did not give the airmen of these units the stimulus of working for a common purpose. It had the effect that officers and NCOs of, say, a unit in Technical Wing were carrying out duties on the domestic site affecting airmen other than their own staff and led to the comment that there were 'too many bosses'.

Another upsetting factor (of balance, not human behaviour) was that some officers, mainly of Technical Wing, were in charge of comparatively large numbers of airmen — which was good experience — while officers of Flying Wing were not in charge of anyone — bad for experience. It may be assumed that this also applied to NCOs.

The organisation of aircraft servicing, which is a major element at most stations, was studied and it was found that First Line Servicing personnel were satisfied at being identified with a flying unit and with their close association with aircrew — although having long periods of inactivity which was generally utilised in cleaning — whereas Second Line Servicing, sited in a hangar remote from flying activities, complained about the isolation. In Benson's particular case, because it serviced a wide range of aircraft types (about seven) it was thought that giving each operational unit the opportunity to do its own First and Second

Line Servicing would be better, leaving Technical Wing to do the more highly specialised servicing. Morale would, hopefully, improve by more work and the return of the old 'squadron spirit'.

Science 4 recommended:

(i) That Second Line Servicing be transferred to flying squadrons.

The Steering Committee decided not to proceed with this, on the grounds that an excessive number of men would be required.

(ii) Changing the organisation from its present three-wing layout to a nine-squadron layout, fully integrated, with well-defined levels of command and with a common aim.

This was accepted in principle by the Steering Committee and, with minor alterations, put into effect.

The aims of the nine-squadron layout were to bring about a clear and unambiguous chain of command from top to bottom, ensuring each section was aware of its position in that chain; to make clear to each section its role and function within the organisation and the task of the station; and to have all activities carried out by a sufficiently small number of airmen for one officer to handle and get to know properly.

The implementation of this new idea was carried out in stages from February to June 1954. Personnel and accommodation were re-organised, as far as was possible, to allow those who worked together to live together (as was done pre-war when the Flights of a squadron each occupied their own barrack room). Science 3 were called in to examine manning levels and analyse manpower requirements. Independent sections were moved into a more sensible command structure. This phase of the experiment was watched closely.

(c) The end of pay parades

The pay parade in its original form was a great time-waster. Men were marshalled from places of work to a central point, usually the gymnasium, then formed into lines on the A-K and L-Z pattern. Then came the payment itself, the deduction at separate tables of sport, garage subs, etc. and the marching back to the domestic site in small groups under a Corporal. If it wasted airmen's time at least the SWO was happy because he used the parade to do haircut and other checks.

The revised method of paying airmen in their sections by the officer i/c just had to save time, and it did — up to 50%. But for all that it met with opposition from some officers who considered it an 'extra' duty and did not want to do it. (One said his job was to fly, not pay. What would his reaction have been to airmen who said their job was to service aircraft, not drill?) This change was one of the better ones and led eventually to 'civilian' pay envelopes and to today's present payment direct into the airman's bank account.

The Stage 3 changes could be called long-term ones; they also marked a turning point in the success of the experiment. The previous stages had been more direct but their content had disappointed those airmen who had expected greater things from the pre-Experiment SROs and Press publicity. The long-term effects of this stage were extremely beneficial, with the possible exception of the re-organisation of the station, which later led to further experiments at RAF Binbrook. But morale, after an initial drop in the first two stages, became stronger as the airmen began to assess the improvements, particularly the JNCOs. By September, practically all other ranks were much in accord with what the Steering Committee had achieved.

Very few remained disappointed at the end of the experiment but there were the usual moaners who resist on principle any attempts to help them. Most airmen, while satisfied with the progress that had been achieved, reserved their judgement because, as they said, they faced the probability of being posted to a station on which little had been done. But of these many were optimistic. One small factor: out of about 80 men who formed the interview panel a few who were due to leave the service could not, or would not, state their views on the possibility of their re-engaging.

At RAF Benson long-serving airmen were found to be lower in morale, possibly as a result of slow promotion. Morale progressively improved in inverse proportion to length of service and trade; the degree of satisfaction recorded showed that lower skilled tradesmen were more satisfied than the highly skilled. The effect of the experiment on internal recruiting was not immediately significant because two factors affected the results: the numbers involved represented only an insignificant proportion of the station establishment over a short period of six months and it was not possible to define accurately the proportion of the establishment that was 'at risk' at any given time.

The difference between Benson and the other measured stations after the beginning of the experiment was slight but persistent, which was not regarded as proving anything either way. However, taken in conjunction with other evidence, it indicated that 'the internal recruiting rate at Benson was favourably influenced by the experiment'. Although the major engineering trade groups of Aircraft, Electrical, Radio and Instrument showed a lower score for re-engaging than other trade groups, more airmen signed on from Benson than from the other stations. And in the field of status, Corporals of the four engineering groups (the highly technical ones, where promotion is normally slow) showed a significantly lower figure for re-engagement than their fellow Corporals in the Ground Signalling, Catering, Air Traffic Control, Fire Fighting, and Accounting and Secretarial trade groups.

Not mentioned so far, but a very important point, is that the improvements also aimed to make an airman feel a somebody, not just AC Plonk, and this (the identity factor) was achieved.

The Benson Experiment ended after six months and then the discussions, recording and analysis began, with RAF Benson retaining all the improvements and continuing with its main operational work. In due course a detailed report was produced by the Committee's secretary, Flight Lieutenant Roberts, for Transport Command and the Air Ministry, containing all the working papers of the Benson Experimental Steering Committee. Science 4 also made a detailed report (from which much of this chapter is culled) and with the C-in-C's recommendation both were forwarded to the Air Ministry where the AMP carried out a critical examination before authorising the recommendations to be introduced throughout the service.

By May 1957 sufficient progress had been made in introducing the reforms to enable the Secretary of State for Air to make the speech outlined at the start of this chapter. However, this was only the beginning: throughout the years more improvements followed, and the RAF gave considerable help to the Navy and Army in this field, for instance with the introduction of work study teams and the adoption of the Families Officer scheme. As the Chairman of the Joint Steering Committee so succinctly put it: 'the ball of reform . . . was rolling steadily forward — and has been rolling ever since'.

This chapter has given details of the Experiment carried out on one station and its recommendations. In the big outside world the routine of service life would go on as usual for a number of years before the changes that resulted from the experiment permeated throughout the service. Part of that routine was to be posted for a tour overseas, for which a surprisingly large number of airmen and airwomen volunteered. There was still an aura of romance clinging to the posting notice, particularly for those for whom this would be the first time outside the UK.

Chapter 7
Posted Overseas

Any airman or airwoman could expect to do at least one tour overseas during his or her service, even though there were fewer areas and places left to the RAF. For such an event in the airman's service the posting authorities treat the event with due reverence — and much administration 'bull'. Today, an overseas posting is mainly voluntary.

The first moves at the UK unit after the receipt of Preliminary Warning Roll (PWR) were to make the necessary personal arrangements for the coming move and later, when the actual posting came through, to find out as much as possible about the new station or unit. The rest of the administrative routine would follow, including being jabbed with the necessary inoculations.

The steps necessary when an airman/airwoman is posted overseas are:

Preliminary Warning Roll (normally up to six months before posting)
Drafting instructions
Medical and dental examinations
Compassionate appeals
Security clearance
Application for discharge by purchase, if received
Withdrawal of applications for service abroad by volunteers
Kitting
Civilian clothing (for certain charter flights)
Pay and allowances
Embarkation leave
Postal and telegraph arrangements
Notification of change of address of next of kin
Airmen's families' arrangements
Record of unit action
Certificate of preparation
Dispatch to assembly station

Other administrative action that might be required includes:

Correspondence and signals concerning drafts
Provision of British passports
Tradesmen's tool kits
Service documents (seven of these had to be actioned)

For a posting to RAF Germany, special instructions were required.

Before about 1955 most airmen could expect to go by troopship — not the most enjoyable way to travel, but it did have the advantage of a slower acclimatisation to the heat if going to hot countries, and, of course, travelling time used to be included in the overseas tour. From that year the steady increase in air trooping meant a more efficient journey — virtually from point to point — and was a godsend for the non-sailor type.

In early days the RAF had a trooping season: men were posted overseas only during certain months of the year (the war excepted) and movement was normally by sea, though some squadrons posted as a unit might move by air. Before the war there were very few troop transport aircraft and what there were were needed for specialised ferrying. For an airman on normal draft, overseas trooping was usually an experience he could have done without, and many had adverse stories to tell of that experience. Contrariwise, others enjoyed the sea trip!

Sea trooping was the norm during WW2 because of the vast numbers involved. The ships were usually overcrowded, with consequent distressing conditions — particularly if the troops had to be battened down from dusk until dawn in their troop decks. As the war progressed the advances in air trooping brought on by the operational requirements of that war, decided the Air Staff to try to make this a permanent feature. For several years after, though, sea trooping was in use to and from the Middle East and the Far East.

At the peak period, the areas available for overseas postings for single and married airmen and airwomen were surprising in range and richness of flora and fauna. But most were set in the standard RAF overseas landscape — dust and scrub. Among the possibilities were: Aden, Australia, Bahrain Island, Ceylon, Christmas Island, Cyprus, El Adem, Egypt, East Africa, Gan, Gibraltar, Germany, Habbaniya, Hong Kong, Iraq, Iran, India, Jordan, Kenya, Korea, Malaya, Marseilles, Malta, Maldive Islands, Norway, North Africa, North Borneo, Philippines, Singapore, Sharjah, Sudan, USA, West Africa.

Troopships were sailed by the Merchant Marine; all the 'Shire' ships were owned by the Bibby Line and discipline was usually maintained by the Army, who detailed as many men as possible to work or duty. Usual accommodation was a mess deck in which would be packed as many men as possible, each with a hammock to be slung over the mess tables — each table sat 16 when all were present — and orderlies were detailed. Among the extraneous duties detailed would be water tap guard, orderly room runner, the mess orderlies, fatigues in the canteens and bars, and lifeboat deck orderly. In war, there were the additional ones of gunners, hammock stowage guards, armed guards in odd corners of the ship, and fatigues in the heads (the lavatories).

With true British phlegm the troops quickly settled into a routine: early wakening, stowing the correctly folded hammock, mess orderlies off to collect the breakfast, wash and clean up and the mess deck cleaned. Off to duties for some lucky people. Standby for lifeboat drill for all. After that it was resting on the crowded deck for those not on duty, with tea and biscuits from the dry canteen and tins or packets of 50 cigarettes. Dinner, quite a good meal for those still having good stomachs,

and mainly a relaxing afternoon until tea, perhaps spoiled by an occasional foray from the ship's WO on a fatigue raid. Troopers were always built with a disproportionate amount of deck space for officers compared with other ranks. The officers had room to stroll their deck; the ORs were looking for any nook, cranny or crevice in which to sit. After tea it was another relaxing period, subject to duty, when the wet canteen was open and the Merchant Marine barman began to make his profit with what passed for beer. But, as the old sweat says, 'there's no such thing as bad beer!'

Weather was the maker or breaker of a good journey; if bad, the heads were full and the tables empty. The first close sight of foreign soil had a real uplifting effect, and actually anchoring in an exotic harbour with the hot sun on one's back began to make it all worthwhile. There was a universal sudden urge to get knees and manly chests brown, often with disastrous results. Overseas had begun.

Attempts were made to improve the standard of comfort of the post-war troopers by cafeteria catering, bunks instead of 'ammocks and 'ooks, and more above water level accommodation, but they were all only interim measures. They were still uncomfortable, with the usual disproportion of space allocated between officers and men. During the Falklands crisis large and luxurious liners were requisitioned, but this is a rare occurrence. The phasing out of the elderly troopers and a reliance on too few aircraft had in fact led, when an emergency arose, to the occasional impressment of civilian liners to carry servicemen. Both sides of the lower decks benefited, the servicemen travelling in a comfort they were completely unaccustomed to and the liner's civilian staff making hay in the canteen while the impressment lasted.

Sometimes airmen posted overseas would go to a UK transit camp — certainly for sea trooping — and wait until the draft was formed before stumbling off, loaded with at least two kitbags, to face a crowded rail journey and the shepherding onto the white and grey-blue trooper to face several days of shakedown in unfamiliar surroundings. Air passengers usually went direct to RAF Lyneham, main base of Transport Command, to board one of the strategic or medium range aircraft. The journey by air was normally swift, comfortable and well organised.

Perhaps one façet of war service aviation that the RAF had not had a great deal of experience in was that of transport flying. But it accumulated considerable experience of flying the Dakota, the greatest of all transport aeroplanes, which had been made freely available to the RAF. Britain's first purpose-designed transport aircraft, the Avro York, had entered service in 1944. First move, until new transports were built, was to modify existing suitable aircraft and the civilian Lancastrian and Halton were so built. The York was in some ways also a modification, using the Lancaster wings, tail unit and the engines, but with a custom-built fuselage, and was the first real heavy transport to come into its own after the war.

Transport Command was extremely busy right from VE day and after much application established main routes through to the Mid

First stage of the long journey by road, rail and trooper for an overseas draft, each with his overseas kitbag (two blue bars) and in marching order/change station order. About 1953.

(Bruce Robertson collection.)

and Far East. The medium aircraft — Dakotas, Valettas, etc. — flew via Marseilles, Castel Benito, El Adem, Asmara, Mauripur through to the Far East; the heavies — Yorks, Hastings, etc. — to Malta, Fayid, Mauripur and eastward, and through African bases to South Africa. One of the latter staging posts, No. 55, was based at Accra, West Africa, and employed local enlisted men, along with RAF regulars, to give them experience of aircraft handling and operation, it being the intention in 1945 to form a West African Air Corps. The siting and operation of the staging posts were hard lessons well learned; the new Transport Command began to consolidate the routes and open up new ones throughout the Commonwealth, together with other staging posts on foreign soil, by treaty with the relevant governments. It was on these posts that so many tradesmen had their first post-war taste of working all hours under all conditions, invariably on a shift system; rigorous and varied work, unsung and unappreciated by the many thousands of air travellers who staged through. But it was a great opportunity for tradesmen to master their craft and show the initiative that is the hallmark of the RAF's training.

Many war surplus aircraft were stored at Kilo 40 in Egypt, a Receipt and Delivery Unit with its own Station Flight, the aircraft in 1946 comprising Liberators, Harvards, Bostons, Mitchells and Baltimores with a few Lancasters, Halifaxes, Ansons and an Oxford. Aircraft staging through to the Far East had been parked there after Hiroshima. Some Spitfires also went through *en route* to Palestine. The parked aircraft occupied a large area and were covered and picketed as much as possible although sudden fierce gales could, and did, cause some damage. The station tradesmen carried out various inspection procedures as devised by SNCOs but, strangely, Corporal Milner never saw a hydrometer used, as they became a much prized instrument for UK-stored aircraft. But, inevitably, large numbers of aircraft were scrapped before the British withdrew into the Canal Zone, by using German POWs to cut up aircraft and equipment with oxy-acetylene

As a contrast to the sea trooping scene, the modern RAF goes overseas by air (in this case a Bristol Britannia shown refuelling on route to the Far East).

torches, smash engine sumps with sledge hammers and axe wings and tanks.

In accordance with the national directive to destroy war surplus aeroplanes, the hangar full of Lease-Lend Harvards at Ismailia had to be broken up and dumped on the scrapyard. Destroying the airframe and instruments was fairly easy, but the order to chisel a hole through the engine crankcase was evidently given by one who had never worked harder than cutting through stale cheese. A 14 lb sledge hammer would have been easier. To any dedicated ground trades the destroying of good aircraft went very much against the grain.

On the Station Flight most of the work was pre-flight inspections, replenishing, wheel changes, etc., including changing a wheel of a Liberator which required Corporal Milner to dig a hole in the sand beneath the wheel as there were no Liberator shock absorber restrainers, 'and sweating blood that the supporting jack didn't slide into the hole! Finally, chasing camels off the runway with

Very lights to allow aircraft to take off and land'.

Living accommodation was in dug-out tents about 30 inches (76 cm) deep, with floor and walls lined with cement paving slabs, the tent pole supported by a concrete plinth and the tent illuminated (just) by one bulb. Hygiene was by the standard thunderbox liberally covered internally with chloride of lime, with desert lilies scattered around.

On sections of the main route out to the Mid and Far East there was sometimes a duplication of effort in that a civilian airline, usually BOAC, was hauling similar freight and personnel, possibly more civilian than service. The duplication ended there, for airline staff had privileges and pay superior to that of the RAF who lived in wooden huts across from the well-furnished airline staff quarters. But the servicemen of 133 Staging Post at Almara (later Cairo Airport) were not in any way jealous.

The ground crew worked a busy day, seeing off the resident Dakotas on their daily hauls to such well-known places as Wadi Halfa, Asmara and Juba, and servicing an assorted collection of aircraft that ranged from Yorks, Haltons, Vallettas, and a Lancastrian, down to the Communication Flight Proctor and Auster. The 24-hour shift had the advantage of hearing a local mullah calling the faithful to prayer from the nearby muezzin tower at dawn. When British troops had to withdraw into the Canal Zone the route aircraft followed them to a similar staging post at RAF Fayid. By a strange coincidence, aircraft that previously suffered from snags that necessitated an overnight stop in Almara were now cured of their rev drops and sluggish CSUs. Somehow the overnight accommodation at El Hamra didn't seem the same as the Heliopolis Palace Hotel. Ah well.

With much of the manpower removed by demob, many of the post-war overseas stations were revealed as the wasteful projects they were — wasteful that is to the new economies of a peace-time air force. Such a place was 109 MU at RAF Fayid. This formerly busy unit stood as a near shambles without its clothing of manpower to hide its defects. But it is all understandable when one realises that the MU had contributed a tremendous amount to the final success at El Alamein; when the Desert Air Force moved

Debogging a Beverley at Wazir in Northern Kenya in 1963. Eventually all the inhabitants of the local prison were conscripted to assist in digging. The aircraft eventually taxied clear. (W. Overton.)

up to Tripoli and then into Sicily, so the golden days of Fayid degenerated as the need for it lessened until it just ticked over. It was the rise of Egyptian nationalism, culminating in the British forces moving back into the Canal Zone, that decided that 109 MU still had a part to play in the overseas role of the RAF and it was included in the long-term renovation of the Zone. German POWs, who were in tented accommodation on the MU, were employed in the work.

At this time there was quite a large influx of WAAF into the Canal Zone, to the major air stations, as well as SHQ units from Cairo. Their arrival caused a reorganisation of airmen's quarters to give the women their own compound, as in every RAF station to which they were sent. It wasn't the best place to have one's first introduction to overseas service, but the women, of course, did not lack company. And most managed to get to Cairo and Port Said at some time on the organised, very cheap, trips to the Pyramids and to Luxor, the latter the visit of a lifetime. And, no doubt, one or two managed to get aboard aircraft going to more pleasant places like Cyprus and Greece.

Cpl Honeybone and friends were involved in an example of Egyptian nationalism. A York had force-landed at Lake Maryut, near Alexandria, and Cpl Honeybone was detailed to take a small party of fitters to rectify what they suspected to be a shrunken feed hose, as indeed it turned out to be. After a new hose was fitted and the York refuelled the party returned to the ferry Anson, where they were arrested by four Egyptian askaris on the grounds that the Anson had landed on foreign soil without permission, which 205 Group HQ had assumed to be needless. Under guard the party slept in the Anson; having no food they were saved by a local 'Smokey Joe' dispensing egg and chips and the following morning, after much discussion, signed documents that 'the last port of call' of their 'vessel' could be recorded as RAF Fayid and not Port Said! They were then allowed to go.

The York aircrew rather spoiled the newest detente by taxying their 60,000 lb (27,216 kg) aircraft over a 50 mm thick perimeter surface, efficiently 'bogging' the aeroplane in sand up to the axle, which made the RAF very popular indeed, compounded by the fact that the aircraft RT was out of action. So the Anson flew out the diplomatic mail along with a very relieved ground crew.

For those families who were able to join their husbands overseas, married accommodation differed radically. In the Canal Zone of Egypt there were a number of MQs allocated for Fayid at Fanama. There were also MQs at Deversoir but in general, as most of the Canal Zone RAF stations were of wartime origin, few MQs were available. Those airmen who, as in the UK, could not get a MQ but were allowed to bring out their families, took rented accommodation in Ismailia, which had many disadvantages. It was a long run by road from most of the Canal stations and isolated from them in the event of troubles arising from the locals, which in 1951 was a definite threat. The financial cost to the airmen was high as the landlords were out to extract the last piastre they could. Although outwardly picturesque, Ismailia had little depth; behind the pretty façade was a squalid town.

The Canal Zone was not the greatest of touring spots and variety of outlook and entertainment was strictly limited to barbed wire enclosed encampments and the odd camel cart. But the village of Fayid, originally the normal collection of mud huts fronting the single road and abject in its poverty, was 'modernised' after the Zone filled by the addition of a few shops, a place to rest and drink and the inevitable stalls. To help ease the tedium of staring for two and a half years at barbed wire and sand, both NAAFI and YMCA performed wonders. Family social clubs, and airmen's and 'WOs and Joes' clubs were built on the edge of the Great Bitter Lake near Fayid and at Deversoir, the northern entrance from the Bitter Lake into the Canal. The NAAFI also ran the Britannia Club in Port Said, an ex-Italian Army building, and a holiday camp across the water in Port Fouad, which was getting rather tatty but was still a nice break for single or unaccompanied lower ranks.

The YMCA organised visits for all to Luxor and Thebes for a guided tour of the tombs and temples, and the Valleys of the Kings, Queens and Nobles, at a ridiculously low price which included an overnight stop in Cairo, overnight Wagonlit train journey from Cairo and several days in Luxor. A trip to Cairo was also on but with the mounting anti-British feeling this could be a little dicey. All NCOs' and airmens' messes in all camps and stations organised dances so the entertainment was of quite a high standard, if limited. The climate is, of course, superb.

Would-be mountaineers in the ranks of the RAF may well have welcomed a six-month posting to RAF Asmara in Eritrea as a place in which to do some acclimatisation training. The station, 7628 ft (2330 m) above the plains bordering the Red Sea, was unique in that all new arrivals would initially suffer from mild oxygen starvation; the effect of the reduced oxygen was apparent to all who tried to indulge in any normal activity within the first few weeks of their arrival. This ex-Italian Air Force station was a staging post with a six-month tour and was staffed from Aden, all postings in and out being by air. It carried all the routine tasks of that work but in addition, from 1949, was caught up in the political terrorism between the Italian population, the

Keeping the supplies coming! Native staff of the NAAFI sort out the Stella and Atkinson beers at RAF Fayid in 1950. (Author.)

former tenants of Eritrea, and the local Shifta, Eritrean brigands whose activities of hold-ups, shootings and robberies against the Italians gave the dozen airmen of the station more than extra work. The conflict going on in the area had the effect of gradually increasing the length of the curfew until it was considered safe to move only during the day until the problem was settled. It must be said that the RAF, or any other Britons, were seldom molested by the Shifta.

However, to give some protection to the local white population, mainly in Asmara, and to recce the surrounding countryside for the Shifta the services of 8 Squadron with its Brigands (apt choice of name!) and 13 Squadron with Mosquito PR 34 aircraft were called upon. Both squadrons sent detachments, thus giving the airmen a sight of a different part of the world which had its own particular problems caused by the late war. Asmara airfield showed obvious wear and tear from its former occupation — bullet and rocket damage to the buildings, vivid signs of RAF attacks on the Italian defenders. The temperatures at this height are almost English spring-like and on the doorstep the airmen had the lovely city of Asmara to explore. Yes, in its day a quite unusual and interesting posting.

As new types of transport aircraft were brought into service and the new-fangled helicopter began to lift reasonable loads, so the expertise of ground trades broadened under the pressure of increased route flying. In addition to this, the variegated politics of unstable countries, which previously had allowed the staging posts on their territory, often meant that these posts were kicked out at short notice and the occupants, like the legendary gypsy, went roaming. However, such is the luck of the draw, some of the posts were akin to holiday camps, occasionally interrupted by the need to do some work. Those laid down across America to stage men and materials to the H-bomb testing ground on Christmas Island (Christmas spirit!) are an example. First stop was Goose Bay, Labrador; second Offut Air Force Base, Nebraska; third Travis Air Force Base,

California; fourth Hickam Air Force Base, California; and then on to Christmas Island. A few mouth-watering postings there, even if the reason for RAF use was that most terrifying of weapons.

AC Dave Bowers was posted to the Transport Command base at RAF Lyneham direct from his airframe fitter's course in 1957. Here he gained experience on Hastings and that exciting aeroplane the DH Comet IV, which included a manufacturer's course at De Havilland, Hatfield. He was destined for one of the aforementioned staging posts. Naturally, all those selected for posting hoped for a plum staging post. A servicing party comprised a Sergeant in charge, two each airframe and engine fitters and one each instrument, radio and radar fitters and ten Air Movements, admin and supply personnel. As AC Bowers observed, 'It was also a new experience for us, working away from the main base on a transport aircraft which was technically advanced compared with existing types, which in addition to the jet engines, included pressure refuelling, powered flying controls, cabin pressurisation and a toilet galley system which was discharged and refuelled through an electrically operated servicing trolley'.

Bowers made it to Offut, a snip posting; probably a number of his contemporaries were envious, but jealous, no. Although in such a distracting territory, work followed normal staging post routine, 'there were very few normal working days as aircraft had to be serviced as they landed, night, day or weekend. During days off or no aircraft movements, rarely more than two together, time off was taken or equipment was serviced . . . The Comet, being such an advanced and aesthetically appealing machine, received much interest from the Americans and in a small way reversed the days when the Dakota was on a similar position. Turnround time for this classic aeroplane was two hours and occasionally it had priority servicing over the Hastings'. The other extreme to Offut would be somewhere like El Adem, Egypt.

In 1959 airmen could take leave to UK (or

any other country within normal visa action) but they had to pay their own fares, make their own bookings on civilian airlines, arrange accommodation, passport and visa. Any assistance incurred to enable them to return to base had to be repaid. Travelling time was granted on the same terms as if the airman was proceeding officially on a similar route. Normally civilian clothes were worn, except in service aircraft (but not for Germany and Austria). The airmen were required to use their own leave quota.

Except for the 'European' type quarters in RAF Eastleigh in Kenya and the superior ones at RAF Habbaniya, most stations in the Middle East had no married patch and families lived locally. The steady erosion of active stations as the RAF gradually withdrew made the building of new MQs mostly superfluous, but in Aden, which became the new centre of the Middle East Command after the Canal Zone was closed down, new blocks of flats were built to the latest air-conditioned specification. The main problem for all ranks in Aden beside the high humidity and dust was the lack of outside activities caused by restrictions on travel. There was less than 30 miles of good roads. Eventually there was accommodation for a thousand families.

A result of losing bases in Egypt and Iraq and the possibility of losing those in Aden was the need to find a suitable replacement for the longer ranging Transport Command on the route to the Far East. A decision was made to build a staging post on one of the Maldive Islands in the Indian Ocean — Gan. Construction started in 1956 and was completed in 1961. The project cost around £5M and was intensive to the point that 11,000 palm trees and all the existing natives' huts were removed — hardly an environmentalist's dream project! But as the runway took up most of the island's 1½ mile length perhaps it was understandable. The station was a one-year posting for about 600 men for whom all facilities except MQs were available, but entertainment was canned, videoed and beamed. Aircraft movements were around 350 per month and a VC 10 could be turned round in 1 - 1½ hours. Life on such a station was part idyllic, with the sun and sea, and part very boring, with the lack of scenery and limited travel. The station was finally closed down as an economy measure in March 1976.

Servicing aircraft, especially on Transport Command, was not just a case of getting down to checking, oiling, adjusting, etc. as required by the schedule. The work occasionally involved difficult jobs for which the tradesman had been trained and in some cases was directly the fault of bad detail design. Often the job was unpleasant and to press the point, three examples are given.

The first involved the Hastings, so let

Two stages of an engine change to a Hastings at RAF Mauripur staging post in April 1953. Stage 1: engine is being removed, Stage 2: engine is on stand and next stage is in progress.
(Jim Hughes.)

Senior Technician Bill Overton (as he then was) describe two of them from practical experience: 'The worst job without question on the Hastings Mk 1 was the twin cables for each control surface. Wherever the push-pull rods of the control system changed direction, instead of using bell cranks like other manufacturers, Handley Page used cables. The twin cables were prone to fraying and had to be changed at every base inspection at 200 hours. It was a shocking job, the bits were inaccessible, the location cramped and claustrophobic — and as regards the rudder and elevator cables, distinctly unhealthy, they were located under the bogs and after an aircraft had been through turbulence, one had often to sponge away the dried-up spilt mixture of urine and Racassab fluid before getting down to work. These cables could be crossed moreover and at least one aircraft crashed due to crossed control cables . . . Another beastly job was cleaning out the so-called septic tanks on the VIP Hastings Mk 4. These collected in-flight waste and AQMs (Air Quartermasters, now Air Loadmasters) were only supposed to dispose of fluids in the septic tanks. However, they discharged food left-overs which inevitably caused blockages which the poor old 'groundies' had to clear. The stench was appalling, especially in the Middle East'. Dave Bowers relates, 'On one occasion a Hastings landed after flying through a violent thunderstorm during which the Elsan container became loose and spread its contents all over the rear compartment. When the aircraft departed all was normal, a ground crew task which doesn't receive much publicity'.

The severe American winter of 1957-58 caused a few problems, particularly at night when the temperature dropped rapidly. On the Comet there were three tanks to fill with water; the galley, toilet and air conditioning humidifier. These had to be done quickly and the hoses drained immediately. Usually the Hastings tanks were filled prior to take-off on overnight stops during freezing weather. The USAF supplied men to spray the aircraft overall with de-icing fluid prior to start-up.

The Far East was a better proposition for married families as most stations were long established, all were near civilisation and there was plenty of local accommodation. And with Hong Kong on the doorstep of such stations as RAF Kai Tak there were no problems about entertainment. Kai Tak is sited 15 miles from the Chinese border, on the edge of Kowloon Bay and serves Hong Kong. It is a difficult airfield to land on as the local village sprawls up to the airfield. Spring is the worst weather period as the monsoon gives way to warm moist Pacific air which causes sudden temperature changes, resulting in physical discomfort. The station has access to Hong Kong and good beaches, and married family accommodation is modern, good and plentiful but now dwindling as a result of the service recession.

Singapore at that time had a large surplus of NCOs awaiting repatriation but there was still the same shortage of MQs as in other areas of RAF occupation and it was usual to hire a local house and then await movement on the roster for a station MQ, which was custom-built for the conditions.

No. 390 MU at RAF Seletar was an extensive unit of nine sites requiring a large staff, the majority local, vetted people. The AIS Inspectors were called on to check and test all manner of strange items, including a locally-built iron lung for a patient in Changi Hospital, engines damaged by accidents on the docks, furniture and contents of broken crates. One of the more insidious aspects of the job was the attempt to bribe them by local contractors. As Ray Honeybone recalls, 'To accept a bottle of orange juice in the offices of a furniture manufacturer is within the bounds of hospitality; to be offered a cash bonus of 500 dollars for a technical appraisal of a surplus Dakota mainplane by a local gentleman with aviation interests in Hong Kong just had to be dodged or the consequences could be a Court Martial'.

RAF Seletar had long settled down from its 1946 strike and by 1955 was a busy airfield when LAC Harry Turner finally arrived in the trooper HMT *Orwell*. Besides the aforementioned strike Seletar had another small claim to fame in possessing probably the largest barrack block in the RAF, possibly larger than Fulton Block at RAF Cosford. As described, each dormitory had 75 beds — 150 beds per floor of three storeys — and the block was 100 yards (33 m) long, so long that a personal invitation was sent for each end of a room to meet! This station held 81 PR Squadron, which flew Spitfires and PR 34 Mosquitoes and on which LAC Turner served (and LAC Bowers was to serve in 1961), an Aircraft Servicing Flight (ASF), two flights of target-towing Beaufighters, a Far East Training Squadron (FETS) with Hornets, a Salvage and Site repair team and a Visiting Aircraft Servicing Flight (VASF). The personnel of these units would leave few empty beds in the block.

No. 81 Squadron was engaged in surveying and photographing the area. A working day was similar to UK standards but the climate meant that for photographic work the early morning hours were best and most of the squadron were usually finishing work early as a result. The photo-recce programme required a detachment to Labuan for two months, many years before the Indonesian confrontation. Two Mosquitoes were employed, which required 20 squadron personnel, and, with a staging post staff and a dozen Australians manning a signal station, in all there were about 50 men. And that meant they had to be fed. And, unfortunately, the age-old practice of a commissar making more than a bit on the side from selling rations had a modern supporter in their Catering Officer at RAF Changi. So much so that the men were reduced to scrounging spare lunch boxes from Malay Airways and Cathay Pacific staff (what must they have thought). Rations were flown up twice a week and, just before the law caught up with the Catering Officer, on one evening 'there was a couple of cans of corned beef and a tin of custard powder only for the 50 of us! Some money appeared and some fish and bananas were bought, so we ate — after a fashion. Fish and bully, followed by bananas in custard'.

There have been references throughout this book of detachments to places over the far

horizons, a commonplace event and to many the opportunity to get away from their possibly drab surroundings or the sweeping grey smoke of rain clouding the English winter countryside. Whatever the reason, and the real reason is urgent enough, a detachment rarely just steps aboard an aircraft and flies off into the dawn. There is a lot of preparation to be done even before a signal arrives detailing the squadron or unit into an area: the need for assistance, and the request; much signal and telex work; the sorting out of accommodation and catering, of fuel, armaments (if required) and spares on the proposed station; how many aircraft for how long; political considerations or implications if applicable; the degree of secrecy and security required.

The unit detailed decides which aircraft have the most flying hours to go before inspection is due, what type of detachment it is, length of stay, who to send (both air and ground staff), and the technical requirements. Should a detachment be a routine one it is probable that a supply of spares — a flyaway pack — will be available ready. If not, the Engineers and Suppliers will have to decide what to take; very important if the new resident station does not carry your aircraft stores.

In the hangar, ground crew will be giving the selected aircraft a special lookover and maybe a bit of an extra polish if it is a proud unit. Wives and sweethearts will be informed, personal kit packed, the old wallet topped up and on the designated day the first elements of the detachment will be off. These usually go by transport aircraft, which is also carrying the heavy equipment and other gear if the squadron aircraft are unable to carry their own. The ground crew would be required to meet the detachment at the next station.

The flight might be enjoyable, average, dull or rough, depending on who, where and when, but at the new station a part of a hangar is usually allocated — unless it's a full dispersal operation — and immediately after arrival, kit, gear and equipment is quickly unloaded and stowed in the hangar — or tent. The arrival of the unit aircraft would herald

Spring (actually much more than that) cleaning of a Jetstream at RAF Finningley.
(R. Phillips. RAF Official.)

the usual frenzy of marshalling to strange areas, gauging the reaction of the station when calling up strange MT for fuel bowsers, unloading any aircrew kit and generally bedding down.

Airmen's accommodation on a large station, such as one in Malta, say, is usually more than adequate and the SNCOs and officers would use their respective messes; the larger the station — and more civilised the area — the better the facilities available. It is on the small, out of the way, stations that problems and ingenuity develop side by side and Chief Technicians, Flight Sergeants and WOs metaphorically smack their lips in anticipation. It may be that the aircraft are dispersed out of the way on some old station operating from PSP (Pierced Steel Planking), and accommodation may be several large and small marquees, used for all facilities. If it is a dusty overseas area it could be troublesome, especially if catering is by open-air field kitchens, as may well happen. If the detachment is to the far north on a NATO exercise then the problems are specific. But it is still a break from routine.

Flying operations would go on and, except for the essential servicing and the necessary tidying up on a site, there would not be a great deal to do, unless it was a crisis detachment when it would be all systems go. On the large stations, problems could occur with refuelling when priority would naturally be to the station's own resident squadrons, although a bowser might be specially allocated to the detachment.

Sometimes the detachment might be given night flying tasks, and the first night on a strange airfield is always a case for extra alertness, especially in taxying and marshalling. A good detachment would soon be mucking in, assisting each other as much as possible, irrespective of trade, sharing meals and duties and, off duty, sometimes all squadron personnel would share a drink and a chat. Pride of unit often allowed this and that kind of original *esprit de corps* often made a tedious task quite satisfying. And left a very good impression on the resident station.

The number of detachments undertaken in recent years means that the RAF has brought the operation to a fine art, so that when a major crisis blows up, as in the case of the Falklands, reinforcements are able to arrive within hours and their aircraft ready within an hour or so from landing at the operational base. Even the tremendously long flights to Ascension only slowed up the plans by the extra length of the flights and the necessary servicing and arming.

The new strategic concept of reinforcing by air from the UK has been reflected in the specifications for the new aircraft with the fitting of, or provision for, air-to-air refuelling. This was good planning, as the Falklands revealed, and it is AAR that is the support for the air bridge from the UK to Ascension to the Falklands, and a posting to Wideawake would be by air. That station has settled into a routine after its hectic period as a supply base when, in April 1982, about 3,600 British aircraft movements took place from this vital island station. Movements are a lot less now.

Two Boats on Ascension has now lost its tented look and accommodation is in Portakabin-type huts, which were flown out in kit form. For the airmen posted in, the main emphasis is on the all-important AAR tanker aircraft on which the whole project of supply to the Falklands rely. Those not on the tanker aircraft will probably be on the helicopter units which have fast replaced MT trucks in utilisation. Helicopters supply the radar unit atop Green Mountain; and from Georgetown, the main port, because of the very high rise and fall of the tide the same aircraft act as ship-to-shore tenders for ferrying supplies from supply ships that cannot use the docks, and have to lie off.

What little indoor entertainment there is depends on social clubs where hobbies of all kinds flourish. Outside recreation is even less, for the beaches are unsuited for bathing and the surrounding landscape is not hikers' country, but every effort is being made to keep the men occupied. Ascension's position is vital for the control of the Falklands: South African bases are greatly missed. Life on Wideawake is a full one; even if the work is

repetitive it is not boring. The tour of six months soon passes.

Stanley airfield in the Falklands itself has been rapidly expanded from the small 'out in the sticks' type to a full operational RAF station, with Phantoms, Harriers, Nimrods, Hercules and the Chinook helicopters under a joint service command. The living conditions are good, if not permanent, and every effort has been made by both service and civilian authority to make a posting to the Islands enjoyable with good memories to take home. But a winter tour is harsh and operating aircraft in the cold weather, which is made worse by the constant wind, needs some dedication and understanding from all ranks of the need for their presence.

The posting is by air via Ascension Island, probably in a Hercules, and accommodation is in Portakabins. Moored alongside Stanley harbour are 'coastels', vessels especially modified to provide relaxation and entertainment facilities for off-duty airmen as

A night taxying Tornado being guided in to its parking area by a torch-equipped flight line marshal at RAF Cottesmore on the Tri-National Tornado Training Establishment, 1985.
(Sgt Brian Lawrence. RAF Official.)

a break from the hard work. Outdoor pursuits are limited to local sailing, cross-country walks under supervision, local hill climbing and inter-service sports. There is still a danger from Argentinian mines in some areas.

Although not counting as overseas, RAF Saxa Vord on Unst in the Shetland Islands nevertheless qualifies in terms of distance and remoteness and gives the public some small idea of where RAF tradesmen are liable to be posted. This station is the most northerly — actually well north of Moscow — and on a parallel with Alaska and Greenland. Journey time to reach the place is roughly twice as long as getting to Singapore.

The 18-month tour on this windy island with a special beauty from its rivers and barren coastal scenery was also barren in other ways. No rail or bus service, no bank or garage and, until recently, no telephone service or electricity, gave the tour a unique flavour to those technicians who were posted to the radar tracking station which watches over the northern approaches of the British and NATO air defence scheme. And Sunday's newspapers arrived four days late. The RAF

Dawn breaks over the South Atlantic and hidden from view in one of the hangars of the carrier "HMS Hermes" is some of the might of the British naval task force sailing south for the Falkland Islands following the Argentinian invasion.

provided the fire brigade, a dentist and medical support. Now that the original islander population is supplemented by oilmen, some of the benefits of civilisation are slowly being accepted. But it is doubtful whether the total population outnumber the sheep. There was in the beginning only one small hotel bar, but no doubt there is a service bar or three somewhere now.

With the number of overseas bases being reduced, the benefit to airmen seemed obvious because there was a longer time between overseas postings and therefore more time in the UK. However, as a smaller air force had to be even more efficient and constant rehearsals and exercises were needed to keep it up to scratch, it meant that tradesmen were more involved with less time at home. So the apparent benefits proved to be somewhat less in practice.

From such places as the Far East and Stanley the return to home comforts in the UK is very sweet, and most look forward to their arrival at RAF Brize Norton or wherever for that long disembarkation leave. During that time the inevitable question will arise in their minds: what will the new station be like? Although most UK stations had a routine and layout that were similar to each other there were still the differences of type of work, operational or non-operational, command, surroundings, distance from home and so on to give each station its distinctiveness. In the next chapter a modern non-operational station is briefly described to give the reader an insight into the life of the average airman and airwoman.

Chapter 8
A Working Station — 1984

Thirty years on from the Benson Experiment, the cry 'Two six on the doors' still rings through the cavernous hangar and with mighty heaves and 'two-sixing' the first shift bend to push the heavy doors along their tracks and past the stops. Another working day has begun at RAF Finningley. This station, situated near Doncaster, is similar to RAF Benson in that it has a range of different units operating a variety of aircraft and has a multi-squadron organisation.

It does not have squadrons of sophisticated fighter or bomber aircraft, neither do massive transports lift off its large airfield. Its job is to train navigators and air electronic engineers, and to convert single-engine pilots to twin-engined flying; in addition, the station houses a Search and Rescue helicopter Wing HQ with second line servicing, an Air Experience Flight, 840 Support Unit and York University Air Squadron. Its products are required by all and to train them the station has Dominie, Jetstream and Jet Provost aircraft, each doing a vital part of the training. To make the station the overall efficient unit it is, an establishment of very experienced junior and senior NCOs have been gathered together to back up the hard-working and enthusiastic airmen and airwomen who do the main work.

How many of the general public, who are able to visit this typical station only on Battle of Britain days, have any idea of its normal daily routine and how the tradesmen and women would be employed over a period of, say, 24 hours? And how many of the revolutionary Benson Experiment recommendations have now become part of that routine? So, with the Station Commander's permission, let us conduct a 24-hour watch on its activities.

While the station sleeps, the guardroom will be manned by a duty policeman and a couple of his colleagues will be patrolling the station (on some large stations a special security guard may be in operation on dispersal, patrolling the operational aircraft). In Station Headquarters (SHQ) the WRAF duty clerk will be available and the Communication Centre (COMCEN) will be manned every minute of the night. The Orderly Officer and Sergeant will be ready for any occurrence and the Fire Section will be manned, as will the Medical Centre.

As a shift system operates at RAF Finningley, the first shift will be aroused, usually by the Orderly Sergeant at 6 a.m. or 0600 hours in service time. Early rising batmen will awaken their officer charges and get them sprucely ready for an early meal. By 0700 the station is fully awake to its first meal of the day, sections are being opened and manned according to the needs of an early flying or other programme; MT drivers, mess staffs, medical centre assistants, COMCEN staff and crash and rescue teams are normal early risers.

The early shift, aroused before dawn, have a quick breakfast and make their own way to their places of work in the dawning light, meeting on the approach roads with desultory greetings. They enter the hangars through the fire door, skirting the sleek shapes illuminated by blue night lamps before the main neon lamps light up, and go to the crew room for a quick change into overalls. In the Flight Office, the SNCO in charge checks the aircraft serviceability from the Flight Detail Board and the Form 700s laid out on the crew room counter, while the Corporals with their teams of Flight Line Mechanics move into the tightly packed hangar now echoing with noise, snatches of song, whistling, the odd oath, the clang of a towbar being fitted into position, the towing tractor.

Engaging a starter trolley for a HS Dominie of the Air Electronics and Air Engineers School at RAF Finningley on the flight line. (R. Phillips. RAF Official.)

As each aircraft completes its Before Flight Inspection by the trades, who sign the F700 and are checked by the Corporal and oversigned by the SNCO i/c, the hangar party NCO checks if it can be easily moved and the towing group quickly connect tractor to towbar. With one tradesman in the cockpit and another at each wing tip, the aircraft is carefully towed out of the open doors where the MT driver accelerates and the aircraft is towed onto the flight line, disconnected and the vehicle driven back. This little operation is repeated 15 - 20 times, depending on exercise requirements and serviceability states.

By 0800 hours, the aircrew are assembling and the flight line party is in position. At 0815 the student pilots and trainee navigators are walking out to the aircraft. The next 15 minutes is one of concentrated activity as pilots do their individual checks, are strapped into Jet Provost, Dominie or Jetstream, connected to radio and oxygen, re-checked and, at the last moment any ejector seat safety pin is removed. The pupil navigators climb into the Dominies and take their seats at the classroom desks; when all is well, doors are closed and starting drill commences. Ground power units are actuated, engines whine and ignite, the soft whine increasing to a loud hum as the revs build up. Pilots signal, chocks are pulled, brakes released and pilots taxy their aircraft clear of the flight line under the direction of marshalling airmen with the 'table tennis' bats. A last wave and the aircraft are on their own. The first exercise of the day is on.

At the same time, 0830, practically all the remaining unit personnel will have walked to work, leaving just one unit on parade for flag hoisting. At this time also the sick, lame and weary are reporting to the Medical Centre, as the old Station Sick Quarters is now named.

As one walks around the rapidly emptying domestic site, the popularity of car ownership is plain to see from the car parks here and there. Even an airman now finds it comparatively easy to achieve on the present high pay — an SAC Band 3 will draw £144 gross per week from November 1984, an increase of 7.66% on the previous rate and that excludes any additional qualification pay.

Out on the airfield before flying commenced, a couple of fire tenders, a rescue truck and an ambulance will have been parked in or near their shelter alongside the control tower, manned by trades with a degree of anonymity gained by standards of flying so high that crash crews can be guaranteed to spend many months on duty before they are called on in an emergency. Crash crews are in Group 12 as Firemen and are a long way in expertise and status from the day when Aircrafthands General Duty (ACH GD) were selected for fire tender work, given 'on the job' training and then spent most of their working days 'bulling' the tender and equipment. Today there is an increasing tendency for the fire tenders to be manned by civilians. A trained medical assistant mans the ambulance along with an MT driver. To keep

their reactions sharpened, the crash crews carry out exercises that include fire fighting, aiding escapes from various aircraft emergency exits and chutes, and first aid. Each man is trained as part of a team to do a specific job in an emergency but is able to fight domestic fires if required.

One assumes that the central organisation of a flying station is centred in the flying units but this is not strictly so. Complementary, and taking most of the load, are the administrative and organisational staff, centred in SHQ. However, the admin and organisation trades have slimmed down as drastically as other sections. By 0900 SHQ is a very busy place with Admin Clerks working on next day's Station Routine Orders (SROs), including duties and relevant orders for all personnel as a result of information received from the teleprinters operated by the Telecommunications Operators and Controllers. Nearby, Pay Accounts will be immersed in supplying computer pay and allowance slips. The section is now headed by Admin SNCOs who, as a result of computer operation saving many hours of dreary work, have been given charge of pay accounts

Ground Support Trolley servicing a BAe Jaguar aircraft on a dispersal pan. (Normalair-Garret).

sections. This work has also been made easier by crediting pay into the airmen's banks. From the modern, well-equipped offices the WRAF typists and communications operators control telex and sophisticated office machines. Down the corridor the Station Warrant Officer is planning with his NCOs for the forthcoming Air Officer Commanding's Inspection.

While the second shift is arriving at hangar and section, some to the crew room, others to work as detailed, the NCO i/c Line Party brings his charts up to date along with the F700s. The flying exercise will last one to two hours and the Flight Line crews will be well forewarned of their return. The arrival of the shorter range Jet Provosts is heralded by their pass across the airfield, which signals renewed activity as fuel bowsers are driven into convenient positions and the flight line personnel marshal the incoming aircraft. As the engines whine to a free-running halt and pilots disconnect their harness and leads, mechanics are making ready to refuel, their bowsers positioned either to front or to rear of the aircraft. A few remarks between pilot and ground crew establishes the serviceability state of the aeroplane and tradesmen begin their Post Flight checks. In the Flight Office, Chiefie is supervising, checking his progress boards, redirecting to alternative aircraft as necessary and keeping a general's watchful eye. The flight line becomes even busier on the return of the twin-engined aircraft with their full crews and for a few minutes the need for concentration is great, as Jetstreams with their spinning propellers and Dominies with twin jets taxi and turn to the marshalling directions of the mechanics. The noise of both types merge to a high pitch and the wearing of ear guards can be seen to be necessary for some.

In essence, with different aircraft and exercises and possibly a different organisation, this scene is being repeated on all the flying units every day throughout the RAF, only very bad weather excepting.

In the case of RAF Finningley, flying activities carry on until the lunch break. In the Engineering Wing, aircraft technicians are

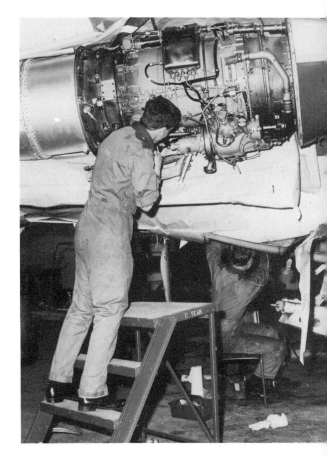

Bristol Siddeley engine servicing in progress, part of the whole service of a HS Dominie of the Navigation Training Squadron at RAF Finningley in May 1984. (R. Phillips, RAF Official)

carrying out routine servicing to a couple of Dominies, a WRAF surface worker is spraying the tail of a Jet Provost, all working to set task cards detailed by the NCO i/c Inspection teams. Much of the Air Electronic work on the Dominies is done by removing the various black boxes from the aircraft to the large Air Electronic and Radar Section (AERS) for servicing or replacement. Adjacent to this section is the Simulator room, where, in cubicles, the air navigators are given simulator training and where specialist instructor training units keep the instructors on *their* toes. All this sophisticated equipment requires constant attention and the AERS has a high establishment of Electronic Engineering Air and Ground technicians for both flying unit and station requirements.

At nearby Station Workshops are bays for general engineering work equipped with lathes, drills, welding equipment and so on, and bays for deep strip servicing of Viper engines and Jetstream propellers. Integrated with workshops is a large section devoted to the overhaul and maintenance of the wide range of ground equipment needed for today's aircraft, under the control of a bright and breezy SNCO General Technician (Ground Support Equipment). The Workshops is under the working command of a Flight Sergeant General Technician (Workshops). All jobs are rigidly controlled to the highest standard and this is a busy unit, even if some of the equipment is dated.

On the hangar floor, in Section or Workshop, on the line or in the office, the slightly formal relationship between officer and man of the 1950s has largely disappeared and although they are not on first name terms — they never will be, at least on duty — the rapport is much more noticeable.

Two Ground Support Equipment technicians transferring liquid oxygen from a storage tank to a mobile ground equipment unit, 1984. (MOD.)

WRAF surface workers respraying a Jet Provost of the Air Navigation School at RAF Finningley in May 1984. (R. Phillips. RAF Official

At main stores, Suppliers 1 and 2 (men and women) restock the racks to establishment in readiness for the monthly stores demand of clothing, and with an eye towards the coming AOC's Inspection. In the technical stores, clerks are converting demand and exchange vouchers — considerably assisted by computers; back at Supply Squadron HQ suppliers are keeping the computer up to date. Attached to First Line servicing and supplying it and Second Line is a small supply section, handling Aircraft General Spares (AGS) and varied small items for use on the work. Due to some unfortunate accidents in the past, caused by 'loose items' jamming some vital part when the aircraft has manoeuvred violently or inverted, great care is taken that only those AGS items, (nuts, bolts, washers, etc.) needed for the work are issued, even signed out, to prevent this possibility. Another possible loose item is a tool and a rigid security system is in use in which each technician has his own tag, which is left against any tool borrowed from the rack. It works. It may aiso be the ultimate of the Benson idea of selected tools and boxes, which they introduced.

Back on the line, the return of the aircraft from the second exercise again activates the aircraft tradesmen. The turnround time is short and there is a practised skill as combined trade mechanics and assistants carry out refuelling and post- and pre-flight inspections. Standing by, the armourers insert safety pins into the ejector seats. The assistants clean cockpit transparencies; radio and electronic technicians carry out safety and functional checks on the navigational sets; NCOs swiftly record flying times, fuel state, inspection signatures and transfer the information to operational boards.

In Air Traffic Control, airfield controllers keep watch over the busy tarmac and the ATC movements clerk records aircraft movements, passing essential information to the switchboard operator for onward transmission to Servicing Control. The aircrew give details in the debriefing room to the training officers and in return receive briefing for the next sortie.

By this time, the Dining Hall, now called the Junior Ranks Mess, is open and it is the

opportunity for some of the shift to get their lunch and the rest of the station to get theirs. Visiting this Mess gives a clear indication of the great advance triggered off by the Benson Experiment in the catering field. The choice of courses and their variety is astounding to an elderly ex-erk accustomed to 'cookhouse food', and is in stark contrast to the catering conditions in 1949 (see Chapter 2). One enters through lounges with oak tables, a polished parquet floor, comfortable chairs and (real) coffee and tea machines, to pass along the servery where a four-course lunch of several appetising choices is ready to be served — airmen help themselves to vegetables. From the servery the airmen pass into the main dining room to sit at one of the round tables, each individually laid out with four places complete with mat, cutlery, condiments, even a spirit lamp. The junior NCOs and airwomen have their own separate tables. Should the airman wish it, he can have a salad meal served in its own dining room; in both areas there are cold drinks available.

All other ranks have a fixed amount deducted from their pay for food and this typical lunch and tea is what they are paying for:

A Sergeant Aerodrome Controller and a Movement Clerk (on right) assisting the Air Traffic Controller at RAF Finningley in April 1985. (RAF Official.)

Lunch

    Soup
    Omelettes

    Poached haddock
    Turkey and ham croquettes
    Sweet and sour belly pork
    Mince beef pie
    Sauté beef and dumplings
    Saveloy and sauerkraut
    Scotch egg and spaghetti
    Saus Lyonnaise
    Chipped and creamed potatoes
    Broad beans
    Peas
    Tomato
    Gravy

Tea (so-called)

    Soup
    Roast pork
    Roast lamb
    Grilled steak
    Pork chop savoyarde
    Vienna steak and egg
    Plaice Anglaise
    Schweinepfepfer
    Escalope of Lamb
    Roast and creamed potatoes
    Cauliflower mornay
    Brussel sprouts
    Assorted hot and cold sweets

The quality and quantity of today's multi-course meals in such that the immediate post-war one-course offering must seem like Dickensian workhouse meals to a modern airman. In that past era, the catering staff had to juggle each day with the pecuniary ration allowance against rationed items and whatever else was available. Perhaps frozen pre-packed food and kitchens equipped with microwave ovens make a contribution to the variety, as a look round shows less equipment and fewer staff that the menus would lead one to expect.

The design and furnishing of dining halls has advanced in parallel, to previously unbelievable standards, from the rather spartan places of bare wood and formica-topped tables with a minimal choice of meals.

Higher standards of training have produced better class cooks, and annual competitions for best dining halls, with related competitions for best products from the kitchens, have ensured continuous high quality fare. Dining halls were decorated and murals painted. When all this was eventually allied to a multiple choice for each course, the living-in airman and airwoman were doing very well, thank you. The only organisation allowed to compete with dining halls on a station was the NAAFI, which has always played a large part in the off-duty life of an airman.

After lunch, the single airmen will probably go to their single quarters, well-furnished rooms each with a good bed, wardrobe, lockable locker, shelves on which might be seen the results of hobbies, study or sport, and a desk-cum-table. The walls are bereft of military accoutrements (webbing long since returned to the stores) but adorning the odd wall might be seen a lissom Playmate. Cleaning of rooms is a once-weekly chore and kit inspections are almost unknown, surfacing only on ACO's Inspection or a similar VIP visit. Bull is an imposition of the past.

Somewhat pensive after this tour and tempted to sit down and enjoy a meal, the visitor is persuaded to go to the larger Sergeants' Mess where the decor is as good, but the Mess has obviously more facilities. The food is equally good.

Throughout the afternoon the station activities described earlier continue at different stages of intensity and without let up. Over in the MT Section, this vital artery in the station's function is feeding in the necessities of manpower, food, spares and communication to all units, as well as putting in large mileages on local runs from point to point, short journey or long, driving truck, bus, crane or tanker, maintaining the physical life-lines without which any station would soon be in difficulties, despite air back up. The trades of MT Drivers, Mechanics and Technicians are among those whose efficiency is taken for granted.

At approximately 1700 hours the last

machine lands and the student pilot walks to debriefing and then to his Mess. He leaves behind him enough work to keep the ground trades going for another hour. A late tea and the majority are free for the evening to go where they please without let or hindrance, subject to not being required for duty and that the Guardroom or Section SNCO are informed of their whereabouts if there is a security requirement. The minority are wanted either for duties or late work. At no time will the vital functions of communications, transport, food preparation and security cease.

Should the stage of training require it, night flying exercises are carried out, manned by the late shift. On completion of the day's flying, the aircraft are prepared for the evening as much as possible in the time available. The second shift return to the hangar after tea and carry out pre-flight checks and other necessary tasks. Well before first sorties take off, the perimeter taxi lights are switched on from Air Traffic Control.

Modern night flying is far less risky and incidents of damage are extremely rare. The training sorties proceed with accurate timing, the groundcrew marshalling the aircraft under the bright arc lights of the Aircraft Servicing Platforms (ASP). The night's programme is completed and the aircraft are refuelled, serviced and probably hangared before a bunch of tired groundcrew make their way back to the dining hall for a late night supper and to bed. In a few hours the day will have been completed.

Following the old adage of 'all work and no play makes Joe Soap a dull airman', off-duty life is enjoyed to the full as far as circumstances, time and money allow. Sport is, of course, the first natural physical outlet. In the evenings, in the NAAFI and Messes, there was something going on, from quiet drinking and reading up to full-bore discos. Many stations now sport a disco club and, as the older generation knows, these are rather lively places where engine test-bed ear protectors are a useful piece of apparel. The modern airman, apparently far removed from Corporal Joe Soap of the pre-war and wartime service, with his hi-tech background, rock group social life and clubs, and electronic aids both for work and play, is basically little different from the older erk. After all, Joe was equally hi-tech in his day; he had an affinity with Sinatra, Crosby and Joe Loss and was fully electrified where it mattered. In matters of pay and conditions, though, the gap was much wider.

With practically all ranks having their own transport, the local town or village is no longer difficult to get into, or away from, as it used to be. Entertainment is now also much more sophisticated than in the pre-war days when a local 'hop' was the highlight. Sergeants' Messes hold regular dances to which civilian friends are invited, as do some Corporals' Clubs.

The NAAFI at Finningley is typical of airmen's clubs in today's RAF; it is opulent and operates under the name of 'The Rose and Acorn'. There is a large floor space, one half of which accommodates at one end a Disco with a sitting-out area; the other half has a bar which many a quality pub would be glad to have, with padded wall seats and oak-type tables for the bigger occasion. Neatly

A data analyst employed in an MT maintenence control room filing one of the many sheets used for this statistical work, 1984. (MOD.)

Night scene on a Tornado unit as emergency repairs are carried out. RAF Cottesmore 1985.
(SAC N. J. Francis, RAF Official.)

fitted into a wall is a compact shop offering a truly wide range of goodies, from tinned biscuits to videos. Upstairs are other useful facilities, such as a hairdressing salon.

A resident unit at Finningley is the Search and Rescue Wing HQ's Engineering Squadron, which services the helicopters of 22 and 202 Squadrons flying Wessex HC 2 and Sea King HAR Mk3 respectively. Here, all aircraft scheduled servicing to minor and major standards is carried out and aircraft documents maintained. Because the detached flights of the squadron are sited around the coast, the aircraft are susceptible to corrosion and to give the groundcrew a sense of purpose some actual examples of corroded skins, brackets and other, mainly internal, parts are exhibited on a board in the hangar. A technically sobering display and the rectification of such defects is an important item on the schedule. The Engineering Squadron groundcrew have certainly a more than average pride in their work, for any of the aircraft that arrive for maintenance may well have been involved in a life-saving rescue operation the day before. Their enthusiasm shows despite the fact they belong to neither squadron.

Finningley also has a Battle of Britain 'At Home' Day Air Show section, whose job is to start organising next year's event immediately after the last. A whole year? Yes, and when one analyses the organisation needed to run an 'At Home' Day of the quality put on at Finningley — and it is not the intention to do so here — one is surprised that it can be done in such a short time.

It was Sir Hugh Trenchard (as he then was) who conceived the idea of the Air Pageant to show the public how its money was being spent. Originally, this was an annual air display at RAF Hendon, then after WW2 it became a memorial to the Battle of Britain airmen and was put on by many stations. Now, only about four stations are involved and the original objective applies. The station opens the doors of hangars and sections and sometimes part of the domestic site to the many thousands who flock to see a hard-working but very efficient station which, operationally, is still almost on a war footing, ready to go as soon as the Government and NATO give the word.

Do any of those thousands when they leave the station know what effort has been made by all ranks to give them the superlative day of

A Tornado GR Mk I (T) aircraft, surrounded by just some of the ground support equipment needed to maintain it in service, at the Tri-National Tornado Training Establishment at RAF Cottesmore. (SAC Francis, RAF Official).

Panavia Tornado GR Mk I (T) aircraft of the Tri-National Training Establishment at RAF Cottesmore on the flight line at RAF Cottesmore. The prefix B and G to the fin number indicates British or German allocation with the fin number below 50 indicating a trainer aircraft. The code number 43+05 is a Luftwaffe identification. (Sgt Lawrence. RAF Official).

flying and static exhibits that they take as a normal right, as they strolled through hangars filled with expensive equipment and working displays, or got in one of the numerous queues to buy the civvy equivalent of a 'char and wad'?

Sheer hard work is the short answer. Planning for the Day is so far ahead that it practically starts almost as soon as the last visitor has left. The first and most obvious job is to clean up all the accumulated rubbish of cartons, paper, etc., that any crowd leaves behind. The following morning all personnel, from Station Commander down, are out early and all ranks carry out one big sweep to clear the rubbish. The sanitation section, or contractor, has the unwholesome dismantling and cleaning of the mobile toilets and it will be several days before all physical signs of the Day have been removed.

During this period, the organisers will have held meetings to assess and discuss with each department any problems that arose; how security was affected; crowd behaviour and control; the flying programme; traffic control; shops; refreshments; toilet arrangements; first aid and lost children; static display attractions; and all the many extra projects, such as fun fairs for the children and competitions, which a crowd enjoys. From all the problems, lessons are learned and recorded ready to be put into use the following year.

Until nearer that time it is full normal routine for the station. When time permits, workshops trades may be repairing and/or modifying equipment used for the last display and, in HQ, officers will study a layout model of the station with a view to further improve crowd and traffic control and emergency liaison and movement. Before summer reaches its peak, flying exercises will be planned with the display in mind. Before this, much telex time will have been expended in compiling a flying programme by contacting other stations and units as to what they can offer. All these individual and team displays have to be co-ordinated with other stations to produce a smooth split-second programme, whereby the incoming aircraft from other units arrive over the airfield at the right *second* to commence their display at the right height and direction to blend into the smooth overall display. Some of these aircraft are from Finningley; others from far away units need refuelling and servicing and Finningley is responsible. So ground crew need to be on the ball with all the different types of aeroplanes that might be expected. The visiting aircraft for static display have to be received, serviced and marshalled into their viewing positions. If training time permits, rehearsals are carried out to familiarise the air and ground crews.

Usually, one hangar is set aside for the static display of equipment and, for a few weeks, there is much activity of stand preparation to put into effect the overall theme of the display, which has been decided many months earlier at several committee meetings. The hangar will echo to mechanical noises, whistles, comments and orders as it is first cleaned, then altered into an extremely fascinating presentation, much of it electronically controlled, of the RAF's advances in the field of technology: communications, radar, armaments,

Servicing a Luftwaffe Tornado GR Mk.I(T) of the Tri-National Tornado Training Establishment at RAF Cottesmore. Note large steps required for cockpit access. The fleet number on the fin indicates German Trainer aircraft. 1985. (SAC Lupton. RAF Official).

inconspicuously by devious paths, removing them when the Display is over.

Finningley is a large station, and has always been a working one, generally in the back-up and training roles. Its own history makes very interesting reading.

Although such a display emphasises the variety of trades and skills and the kind of work that all can be involved in, it is to the visitors a recruiting display of posters and electronics which, while giving information on the service does not — and cannot — describe the types of work and situations in which a RAF man or woman is liable to find

Work on the tail rotor of a No. 202 Squadron Sea King, resident at RAF Finningley for HQ and maintenance duties. 1984. (R. Phillips. RAF Official).

Taping up a section of the nose of a helicopter for a respray touch-up at RAF Finningley 1984. (R. Phillips. RAF Official).

navigation, safety equipment, electronics, night flying, photography, student training, technical training and so on and on. All branches of the RAF are displayed, along with book stalls with scores of books, diagrams, prints, model kits and souvenirs. Some of the static displays are very comprehensive and require large power supplies to operate all the various illuminated or working systems. The inconvenience of having power cables snaking underfoot is avoided by the ground electricians running the cables from the main junction boxes

him or her self. It is these situations that are
the spice of service life, that provide the long-
lasting memories, that provide the change
from routine. They are surprising in their
variety.

*Checks on the Turbo-Union RB 199-34R Mk.
101 afterburning turbofan engines of a
Panavia Tornado GR Mk.1(T) in the hangar
of the Tri-National Tornado Training
Establishment of RAF Cottesmore, 1985.*
(Cpl. S. Ellis, ABIPP. RAF Official).

Chapter 9
So You Want Variety ?

Perhaps more than any service, the RAF has a greater range of operational activity against a constantly changing backdrop; even more so in peacetime, when the service is called upon to perform a bewildering variety of tasks, all necessary and often essential. The RAF also undertakes many humanitarian, non-military actions, not as hidden exercises but from a genuine wish to help the more unfortunate and perhaps to keep in the public eye that the military aeroplane can still be the harbinger of peace that its original inventors intended.

So, after a major war, when its ruthless efficiency as a machine of destruction has been proved and the nations have cried 'Enough!', there comes the task of applying the aircraft and the men to work for the other side of the coin of war. For example, Germany, in her final swift surrender, had left vast dumps of bombs around the periphery of her territory and these had to be cleared quickly.

Bomb disposal

This vital operation was made larger and more hazardous by including sundry Allied bomb dumps, and by the requirement to clear known sites of bombs dropped during the war, which had not so far been removed or made harmless because of the lack of trained personnel. Now, with the holocaust over, the surplus and the buried had to be disposed of, and to the new Bomb Disposal units formed for this purpose were detailed regular serving bomb armourers.

To one particular unit based on RAF Dishforth in mid-1945, and under control of Sergeant Bert Balneaves, fell the task of locating, retrieving or destroying *in situ,* bombs dropped by our own aircraft, usually as a result of having been crippled by enemy action. It must be emphasised that, apart

from the cool professionalism of the armourers, this particular job requires a special kind of courage: the men know full well the inherent dangers involved. One such incident concerned a stick of bombs dropped across a small valley, near the village of Stonegrave, Yorkshire, where the 580lb (263 kg) bombs were found at depths of over 12 ft (4 metres), and in the very wet soil they were sinking deeper. The expertise of the team at sinking the wood-lined shafts was greatly enhanced.

After this spell the section was broken up and dispersed, with Sgt Balneaves doing a stint on a Flying Training School at Godsall where, as the only armament was Very pistols and a few Lee Enfield rifles, he was detailed to a desk job amending the aircraft recognition manuals. Then, as with many servicemen, the Far East build-up had its effect for a number of Bomb Disposal (BD) Flights were formed for service in that theatre, but the malignant mushroom cancelled the project as well as the final conflict. Because of his hard-won expertise and being a regular, Sgt Balneaves was soon to find himself posted to the newly-formed 6234 BD Flight, of which he was NCO i/c.

Within one day of being informed, they were on the move to Eindhoven in Holland, to replace 6223 BD Flight, which had suffered 4 NCOs killed and 4 NCOs injured on 29 October 1945 when Luftwaffe missiles exploded during their off-loading into a crater for demolition. The news had a natural sobering effect. Conditions on arrival were pretty grim, with little help from the Movements people or the local Dutch. The working site was a main Luftwaffe bomb dump next to the airfield. Munitions of all kinds were scattered across an area of many acres, some in such bad condition that they could not be moved and had to be blown up *in situ*. Work proceeded, despite the Dutch Government's moves to vacate foreign forces from their country, and was helped considerably by the Army setting up their own organisation.

The Flight was moved to a village called Harpstedt near Aldenburg to reinforce 6218 BD Flight, which had been weakened by demob and was almost too small to carry on. The job was another Luftwaffe bomb dump. The German Air Force certainly had enough bombs, if not enough bomber aircraft to deliver them. By steady work and skilful application, the job was completed by the end of 1947; the remaining members of both Flights left after demob had taken its toll were posted within 2 TAF, but not before all the Flight transport and equipment had been moved into Equipment Depots in the Hamburg area. At the 1947 New Year's Eve party, Sgt Balneaves handed over the keys of the Bahnhof Hotel and Hotel Hasselmann to the Burgomaster before he was posted to yet another BD Flight, sited between Emden and Wilhelmshaven, whose job was to drain a small lake and recover abandoned bombs and mortar shells from the mud. Some variety in this job.

On completion, the Flight was moved to Lubeck on the Baltic coast, to assist in a sea dumping programme. Train loads of explosives and weapons gathered from all over the British Zone were transported to Lubeck where they were transferred to hopper barges and dumped far out in the Baltic. As the work neared completion, so postings began again. For a change Sgt Balneaves had a normal posting, to RAF Wunstorf Station Armoury in time for the Berlin Airlift, which began at Wunstorf. Because of the urgent needs of that operation, all available buildings were commandeered including all the new Explosive Stores. So needs changed. Because the emphasis was on supplying Berlin, armourers at Wunsorf became surplus and most were posted back to the UK, including Sgt Balneaves who was in time to welcome his first-born.

This account has given a glimpse of what

can be expected from a skilled RAF tradesman; even the most warlike of trades can be turned 180 degrees to help rather than destroy. He, with his contemporaries, survived several years of dealing with bombs of uncertain stability and potential destruction. No praise was given; it was his job and expected of him.

Aircraft salvage

The transition from war to peace was not a clean one, neither was it quick. In addition to the chaos of demob and reorganisation, the inevitable debris of war needed removing and tidying up and among the major items were crashed aircraft, which had been a constant major task in wartime. Now, in the days of peace just after VE and VJ days, the number of crashes was still unnecessarily high, perhaps from a slightly 'careless' attitude brought on by the euphoria of peace or by the introduction of new aircrew flying rather tired aircraft and new aircraft types. Either way the results needed specialist tradesmen.

This was a highly specialised job requiring men who were keen, had plenty of initiative, could live and work together, obeyed orders

A war-time caché of German Luftwaffe bombs uncovered and made safe by RAF Bomb Disposal Flight – just part of the service. Conditions are good for it! (MOD.)

and were prepared to rough it in all weathers. These teams performed an absolutely vital job and their work was little recognised, even within the service. For example, by the very nature of their job, they got very dirty, often had long hair (where could you get a barber in the wilds?), their boots were wholly muddy and sometimes a shave was definitely needed. The SWO of any transit station they might be using, instead of appreciating the work they were doing and showing the Nelson touch, sometimes chose to lean on the team. That was the disciplinary side, but in the technical sense they also were not always received with open arms.

One such team operated out of 60 MU RAF Rufforth between 1952 and 1957, one of a few whose job was to salvage aircraft of all the five categories, and under the command of Senior Tech Ron Milner.

The categories were:

1. Flyable
2. Repairable on site by the station
3. Repairable on station by a MU party
4. Repairable at depot or factory
5. Missing, scrap, recovery of components or for instructional purposes.

As the teams settled down, individual tradesmen were allowed to change teams, so that teams and SNCO i/c became compatible and further specialised within the organisation; i.e. one 'team of ghouls did most of the dirty (gory) jobs'. Milner's team did Category 4 jobs, transporting the salvaged aircraft to 32 MU. A measure of the work output was that this particular team did approximately 100 tasks of all kinds within this period. Part of their essential kit were the twin 'bibles' of the MU, 43 Group Orders and the relevant aircraft Air Publication Volume 1, along with Unit Orders Salvage 1, explosive certificate, clearance certificate and a good supply of Forms 1771 — claims for whatever expenses they could get.

These years being of the Meteor and Vampire era, the aircraft featured in several rather odd recovery exercises, one Meteor that crashed on a railway embankment having to be cut in pieces for collection by a specially chartered Sunday morning train. In 1953, during another job involving the dismantling of an instructional Lincoln at RAF North Coates, the east coast floods carried away most of their service and personal gear. Often the work was cold but 'the cold weather clothing developed for

Although this is a wartime salvage of a Ju 88 in France the methods of aircraft salvage remain basically the same. Only the equipment has improved, well some of it. (IWM).

Korea, but doled out like a desert water ration, was a welcome bonus'.

Just to give their work more variety, the team had the job of toting a tarted-up Spitfire for publicising the film *Reach for the Sky* to various Yorkshire towns, on one occasion to a Leeds car showroom. Because the Spitfire lacked most if its engine, Milner was able to utilise a Meteor nose trolley to ease the fuselage in and out of display sites.

A typical salvage of a Harvard in December 1954, illustrates the team's work. With all the necessary documents plus local maps and special toolkits, which housed bolt croppers, pickaxes, slings and hawsers, crowbars, etc. — these kits were later superseded by one combined kit which was unpopular and ended the ingenious inventions the men had thought up to assist themselves — they set out for RAF Syerston, where they found the major concern was, 'could the aircraft be recovered before the Christmas Grant started?' To achieve this, the CO of the Harvard unit offered 20 tradesmen, which flabbergasted Milner, who chose one Corporal and ten men for the excellent reason that 'more three-stripers could mean divided command and in case of mishap an undeserved can to carry.'

After collecting field kitchen and rations, the team found the Harvard in the inevitable ploughed field, whose gateposts had first to be removed. The armourer secured Very pistol and flares and was detailed as cook.

'How shall I cook it, Sarge?'
'What the hell does wifey do? Oh, put the lot in the pot with water, over an open fire on the far side of the field.'
'How will I know when it's cooked, Sarge?'
'Taste it.'

Because the aircraft was an easy station repair, the team wanted to recover it without further damage. They levelled the Harvard, assisted by the station tradesmen and with the team using their expertise, then began to dismantle the aircraft. At lunch, to the armourer/cook's surprise, the hot stew was reckoned to be better than that served on the station! Or was it the hard work? The aircraft undercarriage was retracted, wings removed and everything loaded on a low-loader, the team showing how to secure the pieces with wire strainers and rope, all of the men working well together.

They made it back to Syerston for tea and relieved comments, the SWO actually smiling, off-loaded then returned to the site to replace the gatepost. It is not known if the armourer was signed on as team cook.

Search and rescue

In the field of aid for civilians, the two things that spring to mind are Search and Rescue, and the relief of those unfortunates in under-developed countries who suffer more than most from the natural hazards of flood, famine, earthquake and internecine strife, which are accentuated by the very fact of their under-development. In each case it is one of the most satisfying duties of both ground and air crews to be involved in operations where the object is to save life and ease the suffering of those faced with nature's perils. The former is the object of the Search and Rescue (SAR) Flights sited around the coasts of Britain in potentially dangerous areas of sea and mountain.

Carrying out routine inspection of safety equipment in the liferaft section at RAF Finningley by Survival Equipment Fitters. March 1985. (Cpl Marion Hamilton WRAF, RAF Official).

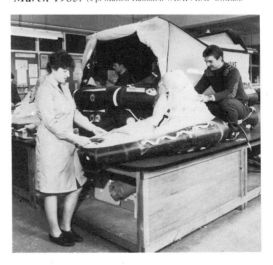

The advent of the helicopter into the RAF in the closing months of the war brought the only really suitable aircraft for this type of work, a task which the service exploited more and more, as experience was gained and each type was superseded by more advanced versions. But, of course, the history of Air Sea Rescue (ASR) as it was then known, began in February 1941. Then the emphasis was on sea-going tenders and these, backed up by suitably adapted squadron aircraft and other services, were instrumental in rescuing well over 13,000 Allied and Axis personnel.

There were no specially-built aircraft for the job, they were all adapted types. Because of the vital importance of ASR, much equipment was designed and used — special dinghies, the Lindholme gear (still used), Thornaby Bag, Bircham Barrel, the airborne lifeboat. During that conflict, the Marine Branch crews performed many deeds of unsung courage, every man giving 100% as the occasion demanded, and they left a tradition in keeping with their maritime heritage.

A Vosper 68ft rescue/target towing Mk 2 launch has two Rolls-Royce marine Griffon engines which give it a speed of 36 knots at 2200 rev/min. The launch is shown leaving Gibraltar and is in fact the launch mentioned in Chapter 9, Air Sea Rescue by C/Tech Phil Brooks. (RAF Museum.)

After WW2 their successors carried on the tradition, though with diminishing numbers. The new search and rescue techniques were co-ordinated when Britain signed the Chicago Convention charter in 1947 — out of which came the International Civil Air Organisation (ICAO) — and in December the RAF Air Sea Rescue became Search and Rescue and the Marine Craft sections became the Marine Branch, operating as a separate arm of the RAF.

The helicopters in present use are Westland Sea Kings HAR Mk3 and Wessex HAR Mk2. The SAR units are not all helicopter equipped; as a long range back-up the Nimrod, although not strictly an SAR aircraft, is used extensively, particularly in sea rescue where its long endurance and advanced equipment are invaluable. Where land operations require greater bulk of supply, the medium range transport aircraft are available. Both types of aircraft can carry the Lindholme lifeboat gear.

The squadrons delegated for SAR have separate Flights at suitable points throughout the UK and life on an SAR Flight means being on the ball, with calls coming in at any minute of the day or night. Aircrew are on a 15-minute standby shift system, as are the ground crew. When an aircraft is rendered unserviceable, or if it has been involved in a rescue where much life-saving equipment has been used or is due for an inspection beyond the capability of the Flight, it is flown to its parent Servicing Flight, as at RAF Finningley, which does the required work.

On today's SAR Flights, there is a high proportion of the Safety and Surface group trades, mainly Survival Equipment Fitters whose job is vital in maintaining the SAR equipment and survival gear so essential to this work. Other trades ensure that the safety equipment of the aircraft, such as winch gear, as well as radar, radio and the comprehensive day and night navigation aids, etc. is always serviceable.

For the far greater areas of the Mediterranean, Shackletons from Gibraltar covered the Western Med, another Shackleton squadron covered the Central

WRAF Electrician preparing the tender's batteries for installation at RAF Mount Batten. April 1985. (Sgt W. Kershaw.)

Med from Malta and the Eastern Med was patrolled by Hastings if required.

Much emphasis has been given to the air side of SAR but seemingly little on the role of the marine craft crews who have been an integral part of the organisation since its inception.

Life on a 60-footer is strictly for the professional, which they are, and their contribution to rescue at sea is as great, in proportion, as any other form of rescue. Once, the dark blue launches were a familiar sight around the coast but, inevitably the Marine Branch has shrunk considerably from its former establishment as the helicopter became more proficient, and more prolific. The Marine Craft Branch (its present title) had been part of the old Coastal Command and had operated generally out of the flying-boat bases where they had been primarily employed for general water work and as standby during take-off and landing of float and sea planes. This last task was much extended by new, and faster, custom-built tenders designed by Scott Paine and tested by AC Shaw in the early 1930s and continuously developed and improved by builders.

The work on which the Branch has been mainly employed includes target towing on sea ranges, recovery of air dropped torpedoes, ferrying, carriage of stores and personnel and security patrols, in addition to SAR duties in conjunction with helicopter and naval craft. A technical requirement for the major overhaul of the craft was that they be surveyed during and after any work and for this purpose a Marine Craft Survey Team was based at Mount Batten; to here, on a voluntary basis, came Chief Tech Phil Brooks, who did not know one end of a boat from the other. He soon learned.

Main trades are marine fitters, boatwrights and motor crew and the personnel were very independent in mind, no doubt influenced by being a separate arm. In fact, as Phil Brooks found, the Survey team were known as the 'outside air force'. They were a close-knit group and had known each other for years, most of them living in the base marine craft ports. As craftsmen they were thorough and superb; necessary when your own life might be forfeit for poor workmanship.

Chief Tech Brooks' job was 'to survey a boat from the electrical side, write the repair schedule and price it in manhours'. To gain experience, Brooks worked on the boats, starting on a rebuild of TTL 2753, and was

Examing the propeller of a Vosper launch during major servicing at RAF Mount Batten in April 1985. (Sgt W. Kershaw.)

helped by all sections who probably appreciated his way of gaining experience. The electrician who helped him had been on the section for 11 years at that time. 'The work on the boats themselves was quite extensive if a Cat 4 repair. This would mean removing the frames, decks and external planking which would be quite a sight; the SNCO in charge of a boat under repair would invariably be a Chief Technician Boatwright. The fitters and electricians simply took all the gear out to leave an empty shell, then the boatwrights started. One pinnace even had a new stem made, this meant laminations of Canadian Rock Elm, which had to be steamed and bent, glued, offered up, fitted and corrected. The carving was done largely with an adze. Magic to watch.

'While the boatwrights were busy on their boat, all the gear that had been removed was either overhauled and tested, or renewed. Then when the boat was ready we started putting it all back, starting off with the electrics putting the bonding in. It was remarkable how neatly the installation of various bits were dovetailed in — with the minimum of fuss and hassle. . . it was at this

Removing the cam followers of the Rolls-Royce Griffon engine of a Marine Branch launch during a major inspection strip-down, at RAF Mount Batten in April 1985.

(Sgt. W. Kershaw.)

Technician (Ground Equipment) repairing the launching cradle prior to launching the serviced tender at RAF Mount Batten in April 1985. (Sgt. W. Kershaw.)

stage I learned that Air Publications (APs) were no use to us — we used the maker's blueprints and wired up to them'. After the boat was 'slipped', it was watched closely to see that the planks were adequately 'soaked up' and after a couple of days it was pumped out, all systems tested and taken on a test cruise.

The Survey Team were required to carry out checks at all the bases, including Gibraltar. It was here that the team was required to compile new servicing schedules and it was the production of one for the Spanish/Moroccan workers employed by the unit that caused a rumpus. The hours laid down in the new schedule had not been discussed with the local trade unions and this caused the eventual intervention by RAF Mount Batten before the problem was settled, all amicably. Because all the electricians were British naval 'maties' and they worked to the blueprints, there was no problem, electrically.

Sadly, the Marine Branch is due to disband by April 1986.

SAR is not all done from the air. On many occasions, one of the RAF's six mountain rescue teams has plodded up remote fell and glen to save an unfortunate, or inept, climber.

The teams comprise volunteers with a hard core of professional 'posted' climbers of a group descended from the first mountain rescue team formed in 1942. It is not widely known that an RAF team climbed Mt. Dhaulagiri IV (25,064 ft) in October 1965.

Helicopters, of course, play an ever-increasing role as back-up to these teams and are used as much as possible, but not in conditions of fog or mist, snow and high winds, unless the emergency merits the risk. The work of the mountain rescue teams is not confined to the UK alone; there are several mountain rescue teams based on RAF Akrotiri, in Cyprus, to cover Cyprus and Turkey, and a mountain and desert rescue team based on RAF Sharjah. Because of the nature of the work, all equipment is under constant review and failure of any kind is immediately put under investigation. As life is at stake on every sortie this gets top priority.

Helicopters are used in roles that are as useful and eye-catching to the media as any. Among them are lifting and placing into position church steeples, carrying urgent medical stores, lifting out patients to a major hospital, and liaison between ship and shore.

Mercy flights

Transport Command tasks include very many mercy flights geared to the demands of peace. A few examples of non-military assistance flights by Transport Command during 1962-63 might give the reader an idea of the variety of the humanitarian tasks of this busy Command:

March and April	Beverleys from Middle East dropped large quantities of food to famine areas of Tanganyika.
September	Britannias carried housing material following earthquake in Iran.
November	Valettas brought in medical supplies to refugees in South Vietnam.
	Britannias brought in relief supplies to flooded areas of East Pakistan, East Africa and Tunisia.
	Hastings and Beverleys assisted in evacuation of women and children from Assam after Chinese military offensive against India.

The transport force in March 1961 was:

Strategic	23 Britannias Cl/2
	10 Comets C2
Medium Range	48 Hastings Cl/2
	32 Beverleys Cl
	12 Valettas Cl/2
	5 Argosys Cl
Short Range	15 Pioneers CCl
	27 Twin Pioneers CCl
	4 Pembrokes Cl
Transport support helicopters	6 Whirlwinds 2/4/10
	15 Sycamores 14
	3 Belvederes

RAF Mountain Rescue team carries out a realistic exercise in equally realistic conditions. (MOD.)

With this range of aircraft, there was variety in plenty for ground tradesmen, plus the added effort of operating from strange — and often primitive — airfields.

One of the reasons why the majority of the kinds of task enumerated above went off so smoothly was due to the precursors of a little-mentioned unit. The United Kingdom Mobile Air Movements Squadron (UK MAMS), based on RAF Abingdon in the 1970s, was initially a section of Air Transport Development Unit in 1958, formed as an independent squadron in 1966 and received its badge in 1973. Its basic task was to get quickly to the centre of any operation to estimate the necessary movement and load facilities on any airfield or airstrip where Transport Command aircraft were to operate. As a result the unit was highly mobile, able to send out any one of its 12 teams of movement specialists within four hours to any part of the world. The teams comprised Suppliers 1 and 2 and Movement Operators and Controllers from Trade Group 18. The squadron motto was 'Swift to Move' and to help maintain that declaration the teams were kept up to scratch by week-long courses every six months to practise the 18 different skills needed over and above the normal air movements trade requirement, including living rough and keeping fit.

A survey of some of UK MAMS' achievements over a year's period of 1973-74 looks rather spectacular, perhaps more so when expressed in statistics, which, though, never show the human endeavour, graft and long hours in all weathers by ground tradesmen. Although materially unrewarded, their true reward was in the relief of human suffering or the increase in efficiency in handling the actual cargo that squadrons brought to many operations. In the following list the weights are in short tons:

	1972	1 May 1972 - 30 April 1973
Tasks completed	670	665
Cargo moved	21,000 tons	20,310 tons
Vehicles loaded	1,900	1,724
Passengers carried	45,000	39,131
Aircraft handled	3,800	3,312

Unloading bags of grain from an Hercules transport during the relief of the starving people of Ethiopia in April 1985. (MOD.)

Cargo moved within the Scottish Islands during the dock strike: 55,000 tons;
NATO exercise *Strong Express* in Norway (eight teams in three days): 7,500 tons;
Tutankhamun treasures returned to Cairo;
Sabre simulator moved from Williamstown, Australia, to Indonesia: 12 tons;
Mercy airlift of food to 1½ million starving Nepalese in Exercise *Khana Cascade*.

The work of mercy continues, its scale of effort controlled only by the number of aircraft spared from the necessary demands of essential training and operations and the cold, hard limits of economic aid. At the time of publication the RAF were involved in moving grain to starving thousands in Ethiopia.

Another task undertaken by the RAF is the photographing of large areas of the more stable countries for development schemes on a national scale. With the modern PR aircraft and facilities at the disposal of the RAF, this job can be completed in a few weeks or less.

This kind of work in the Commonwealth countries often involves special duties; it also involves both air and ground crew in situations where tact, endurance, technical skill, a sense of humour and occasional bravery are required. Quite often, conditions are sparse and primitive, the hours long and resources minimal; the modern MU back in the UK seems like a vision of technical paradise.

Special duties

The Second World War had left Britain impoverished and it accelerated the decline of the Empire, a process that started after WW1. Tentative promises had been made during WW2 to give independence to some of the senior Commonwealth countries, particularly India and some African nations. The first, in 1947, were India and Pakistan, the latter a country newly-formed from the Muslim east and west wings of India. At times like this, when a country became independent and opted to remain within the Commonwealth, they might ask for assistance to help them settle down in various departments of government.

The assistance given by the RAF was classed as Special Duties and developed into the Loan Service scheme through which RAF tradesmen volunteered to serve for varying lengths of time and at varying rates of pay in the air forces of new, independent countries. There were many; for instance India, Malaya, and some West African States. In addition the scheme also applied to such non-Commonwealth countries as Saudi Arabia, Oman, Kuwait, Trucial Coast, etc. Such was the case with Pakistan and its new Air Force, when the country decided to run it on RAF lines.

The newly-formed Royal Pakistan Air Force (RPAF) urgently required almost everything to make it operational. This,

besides aircraft and equipment generously supplied by Britain, included the most important one of manpower and trained recruits. India had had for many years an efficient air force organised on RAF lines, and was affected only by the loss of Muslim personnel who had opted to go to Pakistan and help form the nucleus of the new service.

In Pakistan it was a matter of building its new air force from scratch, out of what could be salvaged from the chaos of Partition and under extreme financial difficulties. Under the Special Duties programme, tradesmen volunteers of experience were asked to serve a minimum of one year, with options to extend annually up to three years, to train and assist the new RPAF to RAF standards. Pay was increased by bonus to make the appeal attractive financially. The whole group of volunteers came under the overall discipline of the RPAF but within that there was a senior RAF officer in command to maintain authority. In 1952 the RPAF was under the command of AVM Cannon.

The volunteers were used as heads of sections and as instructors; they served at the Technical Training Schools at Kohat in the North West Frontier Province and at Korangi Creek near Karachi, at RPAF Chaklala, an operational unit, and at the airframe and engine MUs at Drigh Road near Karachi. Volunteers were mainly senior NCOs and their basic job was to prepare SNCOs of the RPAF to take over their own sections, teaching recruits the RAF standards of technical efficiency, imparting knowledge and techniques on the organisation and control of the various departments and writing approved syllabuses based on RAF use.

The Loan Service Scheme was an attraction to many volunteers and on the formation of the Royal Malayan Air Force (RMAF) when that country became independent, Sgt Steve Powell opted to go in 1969. With another RAF Sergeant he ran the ground side of a squadron which originally had Twin Pioneer aircraft, soon to be replaced by the DHC4A Caribou. The squadron air and ground crew ran on a similar organisation to that in the

When there's a monsoon ditch about, careful how you go! MT inadvertently parked in monsoon ditch at Majunga, Malaya. (S. Powell.)

RAF and the RAF personnel also trained the RMAF engineering officers and ground staff to replace them; the RAF volunteers also ran a ground school for aircrew.

The squadron was much involved, operating against Communist terrorists on the Thai border, annual monsoon relief after flooding, and many scheduled flights. The RAF sense of humour led the Malaysians to regard the RAF 'as mad eccentrics', but 'we got on well with them and if anything I think we left them with that particular brand of humour and outlook on life that is peculiar to the RAF.

'I remember our Malay/Indian F/Sgt at the time of the annual inspection, he was as black as the ace of spades and he got all the lads together and said "We've got to clean up the squadron area so if you'll all co-operate and play the white man it shouldn't take too long" '. Who has the humour?

The Red Arrows

Nine gleaming red aircraft in immaculate formation climbing up the side of an azure blue sky, curving gracefully over in multi formations towards the thousands of spellbound faces, their presence confirmed dramatically by the drifting blue, white and red smoke plumes that follow their convolutions — the Red Arrows are here, dominating the display with their consummate skill. And much more.

These, the latest in a long line of aerobatic exhibition teams from the days of their Snipe, Siskin, Bulldog, Fury, Vampire, Lighting and Hunter forebears, do more than just put on a display. They are an important reminder of what the RAF is about, are appreciated as such and on every appearance must add a few more to the year's recruiting figures. The team is composed of the best pilots that can be spared, who are posted to RAF Kemble (now to RAF Cranwell) as normal routine for a tour with the team.

The flying exploits of the Red Arrows are well photographed, and much publicised pictures of them in action appear in official and non-official publications (programmes, etc.) and are of top standard. Who are the lucky men who have the opportunity to take these pictures? Most of them are taken by the MOD (RAF) Public Relations photographers, who themselves are usually RAF NCOs, but a few private photographs have been used. The PR men are not part of the team, but the RAF photographer is not omitted.

Corporal Dave Edlin was team photographer for two seasons of Red Arrow displays. Cpl Edlin had progressed through his trade in the normal way, an initial Air Photography Processor's course at RAF Cosford in 1970, followed by two years gaining experience and promotion to SAC, when he became qualified to take the 25-week Photographer (Ground) course at Cosford. An apparent anomaly was that WRAF could go direct to the same course, bypassing the APP course.

After gaining experience in his new trade SAC Edlin volunteered in 1974 for a position with the Red Arrows and was lucky: 'I considered it the best job in the RAF . . . All the ground crew, to the best of my knowledge, requested their postings, which goes against the old saying "never volunteer for anything"!' SAC Edlin's primary function was not to take photographs for publicity purposes or even routine, but to use the newly-introduced video camera (then black and white only) which had replaced the black and white cine camera. The object was to make a continuous tape of each display programme and, at the end of the day when the pilots were together, to screen the result to enable them to check the standard and observe any faults. The tape was then wiped clean and re-used. Occasionally, the cine was used to give a more permanent record.

The display season is from May to September and during that period an average of 100 displays are given. This is the time

Red Arrows' spares and trade equipment trolleys which have to be loaded into the Hercules in a definite sequence. All compartments are marked. (D. Edlin.)

when all the winter rehearsals, of both air and ground exercises, are brought to fruition to produce a smooth working unit. The ground back-up party is usually working flat out from dawn to dusk each flying day and when on the display circuit the team, which comprises about 28 men of all trades, moves its ground equipment and essential spares by Hercules.

Loading the Herc was done to a strict sequence, a task in which SAC Edlin and Cpl Roy Marsen, an MT driver, were leading lights. 'The gear would be brought out . . . by the lads . . . who would help us get it on board. First on was the Mini and Land-Rover, which were needed for baggage at overnight stops, followed by personal gear, oxygen and tool trolley, spares and trade equipment trolleys which had each compartment marked with its trade contents, and hot air starters. Jacks, engine stands and tool boards, etc. were at the front'. When all was on board Edlin and Marsen would chain the gear securely.

One of the hard periods, usually a Battle of Britain weekend when three shows were done in one day, is described by Cpl Edlin and illustrates the amount of travelling involved in addition to the work entailed. 'On the instance that comes to mind we had returned

169

from Jersey and Guernsey after a couple of shows . . . stacked the Gnats at RAF Dunsfold and night-stopped at RAF Godalming. The first show of the day was at RAF Biggin Hill, Kent, at approx 1030 hours. The team manager and myself were ferried from Dunsfold to Biggin Hill by helicopter; on arrival I would try to get as near as possible to the datum with the camera gear, the centre of the display where the two solo aircraft would try to cross . . . Show time varied between 20 and 30 minutes, depending on weather conditions.

'When the team had finished . . . the manager and I flew back in another helicopter to Dunsfold; on landing I could see the lads were busy turning round the aircraft, refuelling, dyeing up the tanks for the smoke, and general airframe, engine and avionics checks as required. After putting away my gear and checking the load on the Herc I helped with the starting of the Gnats. The rush was on. When all the aircraft were started the Herc was ready to go, except for the Gnat hot air starters, these were loaded rapidly and chained down to the ramp part of the rear door.

'The team took off for RAF St. Athan in South Wales . . . we followed at a more sedate pace; travelling in the Herc was not the most comfortable way of flying but you soon adapted to the noise and as there was little to do on transit flights we sometimes kipped down for a few minutes. On landing at St. Athan the ground crew were able to get some lunch, with the travelling that we did to various RAF stations the standard of mess food was always good.

'The show was duly done . . . the aircraft refuelled, etc. and they would wait for their slot in the show for take-off along with the Herc. We now had a long haul . . . to Leuchars in Scotland, near Dundee. On flights such as these any paperwork that was needed was sorted out . . . any problems that had arisen from the previous two shows were looked into . . . the answers were ready on touch down.

'At Leuchars we were scheduled to close the show at approx 1700 hours and after landing, working as a team, the ground crew had the aircraft ready once again for the display. I was unable to film this show as I was stranded on the wrong side of the airfield with the aircraft

Closing up the rear fuselage of a Red Arrow Gnat after an engine change, with some of the pilots following the operation with great interest. 1975. (D. Edlin.)

and had no time to get across to the display line. But when the show finished I was able to lend a hand with the refuelling'. Five shows in two days, from Jersey to South Wales and Dundee but amply rewarded by the pleasure given.

In the rare event of an engine change — which did happen — 'it would have to be done straight away or as soon as the spare engine arrived. This would mean the lads involved would work until the job was finished and that could mean all night. But the rough was taken with the smooth'.

Charity

The RAF does a tremendous amount of voluntary charity work which is publicised, if at all, only in that excellent service newspaper *Royal Air Force News*, or in station magazines. Much mental and physical effort is expended to extract the maximum cash from willing participants and spectators.

All sorts of ingenious ideas are put to the test as well as the standard ones of sponsored walks, runs, tandem cycle trips, swimming, ladies/men rugby matches. If the idea will produce money it is tried out. Surprising to some biased people, the RAF Police are among the top charity organisers. All charities are included. In addition, the service charitable institutions are well supported, the RAF Benevolent Fund relying to a large extent on the voluntary payment of half a day's pay a year from all ranks.

Cosford contribution

No book of this nature should exclude one of the major successes in peaceful tasks, that of RAF Cosford's contribution to international accord. RAF Cosford completed building about 1940 and boasted the largest accommodation block — Fulton — in the RAF, which was so completely self-contained that one could easily spend a week there without going outside, dining hall, ablutions, NAAFI all being accessible. The workplace was not there, of course, neither the large cinema. The station was also the home of the Junior NCOs' course during the war years — and the dreaded WO 'Whispering' Smith — and other courses, and

the engineering units on the aifield were served by a single-line railway track to Wolverhampton, which is still in use.

After the war, the station went through the usual vicissitudes and then settled down to Physical Education courses, for which the large gymnasium was further enlarged. Indoor events began and proved so popular that eventually national status was granted until today international sporting events take place regularly and are attended by world-class athletes.

Its other great contribution is the large aircraft museum now occupying the hangars. The unique feature of the collection is the number of 'one-offs' and prototypes — Fairey Delta, Bristol 188, Avro 707C, TSR2 are examples; it is bidding fair to become one of the best of its type outside London.

Vintage aircraft restoration

The museums at Cosford and Hendon attract annually many thousands, who stroll the walkways admiring the superbly restored exhibits. How many give a thought to the back-up resources necessary to produce such a priceless display? Many of the aircraft that form the major attraction of the RAF Museums were not far from being candidates for scrap heaps, or were rusting quietly away in corners of hangars before the creation of the museums led to their salvation.

Many of Hendon's aircraft were stored at, and several were restored by, RAF Henlow, but major rebuilds are also carried out at Cardington, where first-class workshop facilities are available. This painstaking work is the responsibility of the Restoration and Storage Centre. Into the Storage section of the suitably converted hangar come the bits and pieces of aircraft and ancillary equipment covering the whole range of Service aviation history in this country. They come from every imaginable source; they are found in attics and dumps, donated by collectors, or rescued by museum staff. The staff emphasise to visitors that no matter how insignificant an object may look, if it has an aviation background the museum or Centre will be glad to receive it.

These old aircraft are lovingly restored, in the main, by ex-RAF aircraft tradesmen who have taken the job to satisfy their life-long interest in Service aviation. A stiff exam has to be passed and the pay is not as good as it might be. The results of their work, from St. Athan as well as Cardington, is seen in the museums of Hendon, Cosford and Manchester and it does not need a close scrutiny to see how good the restoration work is. This kind of work is also carried out on a voluntary basis by regular RAF units to help ease the cost of the work and it may be these jobs that generate the subsequent enthusiasm. It is certainly a contrast to have been working on, say, a Jaguar during the day and in the evening turn to restoring work on a DH9A.

A recent example was the major inspection and refurbishing of the Battle of Britain Memorial Flight Lancaster by B Flight of No. 1 Aircraft Servicing Squadron at RAF Abingdon. In the course of the work, which ranged from October 1983 to April 1984, the aircraft received probably the most comprehensive overhaul any has had since the war. The Lancaster was completely stripped — even the fuselage was divided into its three component parts — and every inch of the construction checked for signs of fatigue and corrosion. The work was made much more difficult by the lack of technical documents, Air Publications and, of course, spares. Of the former a combination of available literature, manufacturers' help and good old-fashioned expertise succeeded; in the latter case some spares had to be made from drawings, others were replaced by modern equivalent items.

Because of the size of the task and the deadline — which was met — the work was shared; RAF Coningsby overhauled the Merlins, RAF St. Athan helped with tanks and components, several civilian firms mucked in with new perspex windscreens, radiator repairs, fuel and hydraulics. No special training was required, the standards of RAF engineering skills being sufficient, but to the young tradesmen the mighty Lanc must have seemed somewhat of a dinosaur against a Jaguar or Tornado. The job was a huge success and on successful completion of

checks, tests and flight tests, No.1 Aircraft Maintenance Squadron had given to the Battle of Britain Memorial Flight an aircraft that will be able to delight the crowds up to the end of this century, at its present rationed flying hours per year.

Missile operation

From the sublime majesty of the old to the one-shot killing techniques of the new via the present generation of surface to air missiles (SAM), brings a taste of variety in operating a system that may yet supersede aircraft in their currently developed versions. Already the long range ballistic missiles can do just that but they suffer from the need for fixed installations, which the Tornado and others combat by their flexibility of operation. But Cruise is significant.

American Thor Intercontinental Ballistic Missile medium range, 60 of which were supplied to the RAF during the Sandys period of 'no manned bombers' in 1959.
(Bruce Robertson collection.)

First of the missile breed into RAF service in 1959 was Thor, an American ballistic missile introduced as a result of the 1957 theory that 'the manned bomber was finished'. First RAF tradesmen for these weapons were sent to America for manufacturers' courses, among them being Sgt J. P. Hurst, who enjoyed a pleasant ten-day sea trip and then cross-country by train from Halifax, Nova Scotia, to Tucson, Arizona. After a course which included enough misfortunes, such as missiles blowing up, to cause a General 'Smiling Jack' to make the pithy comment 'Oh, shit', Sgt Hurst returned home to join one of the Strategic Missile (SM) squadrons, 77, 98, 113. Much time was spent on operational exercises, including the major one where the missile launch was taken up through four stages of pre-ignition. The fifth was the ignition stage. It went like this:

Phase 1

On the turn of a switch in the Launch Control Trailer (LCT) the generators would come on line and the countdown begin. This was a check-out phase of circuits aligning the gyro platform and a trial show of the engine (main and the two verniers). About $3\frac{1}{2}$ minutes.

Phase 2

The shelter would automatically retract from the missile. When clear the missile would be hydraulically raised from horizontal to the vertical. The missile cradle would be lowered. About $3\frac{1}{2}$ minutes.

Phase 3

Liquid Oxygen (LOX) and Rocket Kerosene Propellant 1 (RP-1) would be transferred from outside tanks into the respective tanks in the missile with the assistance of compressed nitrogen at 95 psi. Six minutes.

Phase 4

Transfer of electrical power from external to internal power. Up to 45 seconds.

Phase 5

Ignition stage. Up to 45 seconds.

Bloodhound air-to-air Mk 2 missiles lined up at RAF West Raynham and backed up by radar at rear during 1976. These missiles are still in service. (MOD.)

Sgt Hurst thought the missile reliable but vulnerable because the outside skin of the missile was in part also the tank skin and very susceptible to a single bullet. He also thought that very few on Thor enjoyed the job. To a more light-hearted point, although it really was serious, was the more suspect security on the bases. In an article in the *RAF Review* of 1960 the author Peter Williams is quoted as saying, that, during a practice launch,' . . . a RAF dog handler with dog was nearby for security . . . '. Shades of Greenham Common. At that time the highly skilled handling by the tradesmen of these missiles was of the utmost importance to the country.

In 1957 Britain's first SAM, the Bloodhound Mk 1, entered service and its Mk 2 derivative has so remained ever since. The missile is a semi-active homing type guided by radar beam projected at the target which is reflected back to guidance equipment housed in the nose in front of the warhead. Initial launch is provided by four solid fuel rockets secured by quick release devices, and on their jettisoning after launch the missile is powered by two Bristol ramjets. A squadron of missiles requires a high proportion of electric/electronic ground and air technicians, in addition to airframe, rocket motor, radar and weapon technicians.

A Rapier surface-to-air missile being sited by an Army team. This missile is in use by the RAF Regiment and is highly mobile and effective. They served with distinction in the Falklands campaign. (Bruce Robertson collection.)

RAF North Coates, first home of the Bloodhound, was a four-wing organisation with Administration, Technical, Operations and Trials Planning and Assessment Wings. The Technical wing was divided into two squadrons, Central Servicing and Radar, and control was exercised through the Technical Control section which, like aircraft servicing, maintained all servicing records and modification state. First line servicing was done by squadrons and second line by the Wing; squadrons serviced by replacement and the sub-assemblies were sent to the Wing, which was also responsible for maintaining a stock of required spares in conjunction with the Equipment Section.

The much improved Bloodhound Mk 2 was fully mobile and air transportable, which allowed the weapon to be sent to selected areas overseas. Mobility, however, was only in the ability to change site rather than in the accepted meaning of the word. The weapon

No. 22 Squadron of the RAF Regiment carrying out an exercise with a Rapier ground-to-air missile section at RAF Leuchars. A Phantom taking off. 1976. (MOD.)

Tigercat, precursor of the Rapier, in a defence capacity exercise in 1970. These missiles are now phased out. (MOD.)

was deployed to the Middle East, Malaya and Germany and although never used in anger it has stood up very well to the climatic conditions in those countries. It is still in service.

Now a lighter, highly mobile SAM, the Rapier, has been issued to the RAF Regiment for airfield defence, and is used by both RAF and Army. This weapon is in extensive use by the Regiment and is deployed in Germany. Its adoption has raised the technical level on many Regiment squadrons, which was previously derided in some areas as less than technical, a quite unfounded criticism for the Regiment at times has had to handle quite sophisticated weapons. The test of their ability comes when an airfield is under attack and in the Falklands the Rapier sections hammered home their reply, bending a few Argentine aircraft. They certainly had variety.

It is quite possible with the present speed of

development of micro electronics that Mr. Sandys' forecast of an all-missile force may yet be proved right. Cruise appears to be the first step. With Britain possessing no land-based ballistic missile force, and so relying on the manned bomber, the future of that aircraft is reasonably assured for some time, particularly for strategic delivery of the nuclear bomb. But the development of the automatic, unpiloted flying bomb/missile is proceeding at such a pace — together with the anti-missile missile — that soon the strategic bomber as such will be obsolescent and the ballistic missile will take precedence again. But when and if it does come, it will not be introduced in such a way as to weaken other arms of the service but will be complementary to them. Either way, ground tradesmen will be required and some may see it as the ultimate accolade — an all ground staff operated strategic deterrent.

Chapter 10
You do need Institutions

Almost 40% of the RAF air and ground crews have gained their first insight into the service through one of the oldest institutions, the Air Training Corps (ATC), via their local ATC squadron. Although not strictly a part of the RAF the ATC is often a direct lead into that service for younger men by virtue of the experiences it offers, its affiliations and its aims. Many of the ATC instructors are ex-RAF, although the majority of the officers are civilians under the RAF Volunteer Reserve (T) scheme.

The staff of the squadrons do a great job: the variety of indoor and outdoor activities provided is wide, affording an outlet for a youngster's energies and interests, most culminating in Duke of Edinburgh Awards and other national and local competitions, but there is an overall bias towards the RAF. The service itself encourages air-mindedness by having Air Experience Flights on some stations (although many cadets are flown in civilian aircraft), annual visits of ATC squadrons, events on the station and so on. From experience, the yearly ATC camp on a service station, with the Chipmunk or whatever aircraft, tents and general air of youthful enthusiasm and exuberance is as

'NAAFI up'. Mobile NAAFI van serves one of several hundred queues that formed up, or did, each morning throughout the UK. Despite the tea, it was always welcome. This scene is at RAF Oakington in May 1954. (NAAFI.)

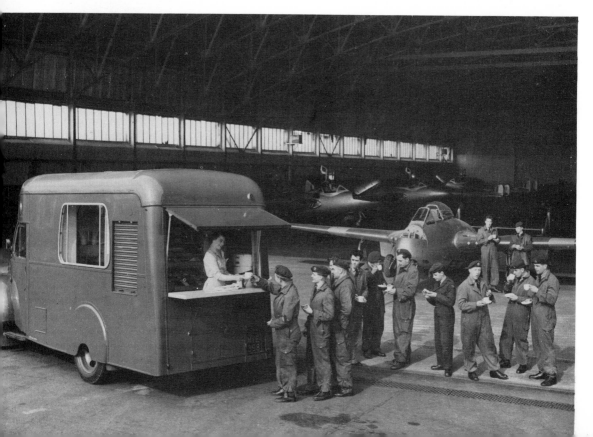

much appreciated by the old hands as by the participants. Which is all as it should be.

It is a good scheme and the RAF has been enriched by the young volunteer products of usually first class staff. However, the primary aim of the ATC is *not* to provide recruits for the RAF but to be a voluntary youth movement providing valuable training that will be of great use in adult life. It is obvious though, and well proven, that cadets who want to join and have a sound basic knowledge of the RAF are of great benefit to the service.

After an airman's recruit and technical training his first service years on a unit will be ones combining learning and enjoyment; during that period the NAAFI will play as great a part as it did in his training days. It might be appropriate at this point to give a brief discription of this institution, essential to service men and women because it is so much an accepted part of service life. Just

about everyone has had cause to praise it at least once in his service.

The NAAFI (Navy, Army and Air Force Institute) was born on 1 January 1921 out of an earlier wish by a Major Crauford and a Surgeon Captain Murray to get fair play in the off-duty time of other ranks. The two men went ahead to form the Canteen and Mess Co-operative Society in 1894. From this developed the Expeditionary Forces Canteen in 1914, to be renamed the Navy and Army Canteen Board, at which juncture the RAF joined it in 1918. Finally, in March 1920, Winston Churchill appointed an inter-departmental committee to consider a permanent Forces Canteen and the NAAFI came into being.

That branch of NAAFI serving the RAF did a fine job — given the difficulties of the times and despite the quality of the tea! By its integration with the RAF — as with the other two services — other ranks were intimately

Cadets of No. 162 ATC Squadron assembling a Vampire TII at Hazel Grove Secondary School in July 1975. Out of this group the following trades and professions were filled: taxman, engineer, design engineer, policeman and F/Lt RAF. (Advertiser Express.)

concerned not only in sharing its benefits but also in giving material assistance in the running and maintenance of their unit NAAFI. This is the responsibility of the parent service; part of the duties of the Orderly Corporal was to see that the bar was closed at the proper times, all airmen left at closing time and that the place was securely locked. If staff lived on the premises they would be included under any security arrangements.

NAAFI are to be found on the most isolated of sites and did a magnificient job under the most adverse of conditions during the war. In fact in most wars, although during the earlier ones there was an opportunity for some canteen staff to make a bit on the side. After WW2 NAAFI slipped back naturally into a routine. However, to keep up with the rising expectations of airmen, it soon began to adopt a more club-like atmosphere; the old pre-war and immediate post-war image of NAAFI with its sparse furniture of small tables and cane chairs set in a decor of brown and green has vanished, to be replaced by a club style never to be imagined in those days. As far as possible all facilities are shared by both sexes. The Corporals have a similar facility where their mess is a part of NAAFI.

In the course of progress the existing standard canteens were adapted, revised, redesigned and rebuilt into social clubs. The sales facilities available to airmen are really tremendous — the full list would take up a lot of space, so here are just half a dozen examples: Cars can be bought and insured; life assurance policies are arranged; flowers can be sent by Interpost; instalment credits are arranged; a whole wardrobe of clothes can be purchased off the peg; and automated 24-hour cafeterias offering food, drink and cigarettes are in service.

In the Middle East in the 1950s, NAAFI used a large caravan-type trailer, towed by a prime mover and filled with all manner of goodies, not normally on sale in the station NAAFI shops, to travel around the various service units, which proved most successful.

Over 500 NAAFI staff have been killed by enemy action and over 100 decorated for gallantry, the last in the recent Falkland Islands campaign where it was in the forefront and where there is now a branch at RAF Stanley to give a degree of comfort and service. The NAAFI is run as a modern business and is more successful than most in spite of its policy of ploughing its profits back into the services. Amongst all the advanced hi-tech and sophistication the demands on the NAAFI organisation have remained basically the same: it is one institution that has retained a particular affection among all other ranks.

It is almost certain that at some time our young service men and women are going to visit London, either on leave or in an official capacity. Either way, many will opt to stay at the Union Jack Club (UJC) for its cheapness, its handy position and because of its service orientation. This is an institution that has long been of the utmost worth to the ordinary service man and woman.

The Boer War began a process for people in this country: that of discovering that servicemen are normal people, with normal intelligence and emotions, who like to be treated as such, rather than being dismissed as scum. Life in India in the ranks pre-20th century is an example: the men were completely ignored off-duty and found their pleasure mainly in the wet canteen — the originators of those canteens provides one example of responsible men trying to help. Service life in South Africa was influenced by the high proportion of recruits coming from a civilian life that was steadily improving.

There were advanced minds in the service hierarchy who observed this, understood the trend and tried to improve the lot of the lower ranks off-duty, as with NAAFI. One of these was the need for adequate leave accommodation where there was a reasonable bed and food at prices they could afford. Such a place — and a large grand place it was — was built for them in Waterloo Road and was originally conceived as a working memorial to those who fell in the Boer War. In 1904 the foundation stone was laid and on 1 July 1907 the Club was opened by King Edward VII and Queen Alexandra and patriotically named the Union Jack Club.

It was a service 'hotel' in advance of its time, magnificently built with some architectural quality, with 355 small rooms, each containing an iron locker on the wall, spring (?) bed, washhand stand, hooks, mirror and mat. All amenities then in vogue including hot baths were provided at small cost, and a large dining room serving a variety of wholesome service type food was quite popular. As time passed, and as a result of two major world wars, a steady programme of improvement and expansion was undertaken. The number of beds reached 816 and, with an Annexe, finally went up to 1100. Countless thousands of servicemen — and later, women — had cause to thank this great club for its welcome to them. No one was turned away if there was a bed.

But, as with all, time caught up with the Union Jack Club of 1907. It began to look like an 'institution' and the increased costs and very expensive maintenance of the fabric in the new era of 'cost-effectiveness' decided the council that a new UJC was needed and now (1971) was the time. So in that year the old club was demolished and a graceful modern structure, incorporating a Married Families section, was raised on the original site and opened by Queen Elizabeth II on 12 February 1976.

The new building brings off-duty service accommodation bang into this century, and the next, and is a tremendous advance, with modern amenities and an entrance layout and decor the equal of any hotel of its class. Each of the 417 single and 63 double bedrooms has hot and cold water, wardrobes, shaving sockets, lights and mirrors, electronic clock with alarm, all-carpeted floor and adequate bed. Each floor is complete with showers and baths and all up-and-down movement to the 24 floors is by lift in this warm brick and smoked-glass building. A cafeteria-type restaurant replaces the old dining room, with a variety of dishes that reflects the modern trend of today's service cuisine. A well-stocked modern bar is available for both sections and women are automatically members, with some membership to ex-servicemen on a time served basis. From the windows of the many bedrooms the occupants have extremely good views across London, and, being sited opposite Waterloo railway station, what could be handier? Unfortunately, there is no provision for car parking.

A final word sums up the outlook of those who built and organise this delightful hotel. 'It is not, as some believe, a Ministry of Defence establishment, but a completely independent charity. This does not mean that it is in the business to distribute charity to service men and women but simply that it is not required to make a profit beyond that needed to cover its operational costs, nor is it subject to taxes which a profit-making company has to pay.' Somewhat similar to NAAFI.

As our former recruits mature and become wise in the ways of the service, so the thoughts of a number of long serving types begin to veer towards the idea of membership of the Corporals' and Sergeants' Messes. Natural enough. To enter these places, service establishments rather then institutions, is a right that has to be earned. It is a first positive step up the ladder.

A typical Sergeants' Mess lounge of the immediate post-war period at RAF Marham, 1945. (Author.)

Sergeants' Mess bar of today shows the high standard of furnishing which is expected and now normal. The rest of the Mess conforms. This is at RAF Finningley and most other stations are similar. April 1985. (RAF Official.)

The Corporals' Messes had a rather fluctuating progress. In the years before the war the authority of Corporals was normally accepted by right of experience and long service within a small air force. Most stations allowed a Corporals' Mess in a part of the NAAFI, some even in a separate hut; there was a separate bunk attached to each barrack room and, sometimes, a few separate tables in the dining room.

The hard-earned status was eroded during the war and immediately after when the pre-war title of 'can carriers' became more appropriate. During WW2 the massive increase in manpower, with resultant increase in promotions, gave rise to more Corporals than there were privileged facilities for — to the detriment of stable authority. On those stations that still had Messes they sometimes degenerated into just rest rooms. After WW2 peacetime regulations, plus an advance in conditions, assured that Corporals' Messes were established on properly-run lines similar to the Sergeants' Messes, with duties in the Mess and committees controlled by themselves.

Promotion from Coporal is relatively quick in the post-war air force subject to qualifications and time served, plus the all-important recommendation. Entering the Sergeants' Mess, probably for the remainder of his service, is a major advance up the ladder. Those who do so experience the best of service life. Sergeants' Messes are well-organised social and living quarters usually of a very high standard of comfort and behaviour. Meals are taken in near-restaurant surroundings and prepared by kitchen staff who could take over the Savoy *en bloc* without a noticeable hiccup in that hotel's service.

But the immediate post-war overfull establishment of SNCOs on most stations had led to problems of serious overcrowding, a situation made worse by the large number of NCO aircrew of those days. Originally, the RAF had decided to re-title the aircrew ranks and give them their own Mess, which however did not take off! The old ranks were retained. The later concept of making all aircrew commissioned officers successfully solved the accommodation problem in general, even though there was still doubling up in some Messes. Finally, some Messes that had been 'borrowed' for officer use during the war were returned. The crowded conditions meant varying degrees of discomfort, dining rooms so full that breakfast latecomers seriously risked missing morning parade. But whatever the problems all members were responsible for the running of their own mess and to press the point all (or nearly all) were eligible for the various duties laid down to maintain that responsibility.

The job of Mess Treasurer is normally a Flt Sgt's or Chief Tech's duty and to him falls the dubious job of keeping the Mess accounts accurate and healthy, making up the monthly Mess bills — and seeing they are paid — answering any finance questions at Mess meetings and ensuring the Officer i/c is kept happy. He is also responsible for dealing with outside customers; outside purchases; messing and casual meals for visitors; petty cash holding, and so on.

An essential requirement of any healthy thriving Mess is a good Entertainment

Committee, upon whose judgement depends to a large extent the quality of the Mess social life. Any Mess near a large town is facing competition, but with skilled application many good dances and socials can be organised to the financial benefit of the Mess, through the bar takings which is where it matters. The conduct of the Mess and its members is influenced both by the senior members and a lively Mess Committee who see that the Mess is run properly, is well maintained, is kept clean and that all external buildings belonging to the Mess such as sleeping quarters are looked after. They also keep an unobtrusive eye on conduct during occasions when the wine might be running in plenty!

Mess meetings can be, and often are, lively as, under the authoritative eyes of the Chairman of the Mess Committee (CMC), SWO, Treasurer and sometimes the Officer i/c, subject questions are fired on general messing, debit and credit, mess bills, forthcoming entertainments, purchases, depreciation of property and any matter of Mess discipline and etiquette. Surprisingly large sums of money can be voted for worthwhile projects. No profits are contemplated, other than from the bar. When the 'goggle box' began its insidious mesmerism every Mess purchased one, which meant a TV room had to be provided and furnished.

Several times a year full-scale Mess dances are usually organised, to which are invited the station CO, his officers and their wives, and special guests, and every SNCO not on duty or leave is expected to attend. The Mess cook/chef, usually with help from the WO caterer, often performs feats of gastronomic skills. If the Mess is situated near a town it is also normal to hold dances and social functions to which the local townsfolk are invited; buffets are usually laid on. The Sergeants' Mess is indeed the ultimate residence for other ranks.

Retirement from the RAF brings the mixed feelings that almost everyone experiences, irrespective of age and background. With ex-RAF types there is usually a strong sense of leaving a job that has given more than just work satisfaction; they have spent most of their lives in the company of like-minded companions. After the initial settling down process in civvy street there comes to many the wish to mix again with ex-RAF types. So they join the local branch of the Royal Air Forces Association (RAFA), the last institution to be mentioned in this chapter.

The RAFA is so well known an organisation that no attempt will be made to describe its activities in detail, which are basically charitable; suffice it to say that in most branches the spirit of 'the good old days' can still be experienced, albeit that it is the spirit of WW2 that stimulates the majority of members rather than that of Aden, Malaya or Kenya. But conversion is steadily taking place as more post-WW2 airmen join.

There are hundreds of branches nationwide, and overseas, most doing a wonderful job for their less fortunate members and maintaining a welcoming atmosphere in which men like ex-Flt Sgt Joe Soap can meet old friends and reminisce. Indeed one of the most useful institutions of all.

Index

1/1/100